my legs are crying

WHAT A PEDIATRICIAN LEARNED ABOUT EMOTIONALLY-BASED ILLNESS

Maggie Kozel, MD

First Stillwater River Publications Edition

ISBN: 978-1-960505-06-4

Library of Congress Control Number: 2023903846

1 2 3 4 5 6 7 8 9 10
Written by Maggie Kozel, MD.
Cover design by Elisha Gillette.
Interior book design by Matthew St. Jean.
Published by Stillwater River Publications, Pawtucket, RI, USA.

Names: Kozel, Maggie, 1955- author.
Title: My legs are crying : what a pediatrician learned about emotionally-based illness / Maggie Kozel, MD.
Description: First Stillwater River Publications edition. | Pawtucket, RI, USA : Stillwater River Publications, [2023]
Identifiers: ISBN: 978-1-960505-06-4 | LCCN: 2023903846
Subjects: LCSH: Sick children--Psychology. | Medicine, Psychosomatic. | Emotions in children--Health aspects. | Pediatrics--Psychological aspects. | Child psychology. | Depression in children. | Anxiety in children.
Classification: LCC: RJ47.5 .K69 2023 | DDC: 618.9200019--dc23

To the patients of Hasbro's sixth floor,
who proved that you are never too young to inspire,
or too experienced to learn.

Author's Note

ALL THE CLINICAL PRESENTATIONS I DESCRIBE IN THIS book are ones I actually encountered either in my outpatient practice or in the MedPsych program at Hasbro Children's Hospital, and I accurately describe them to the best of my memory. I do, however, use composite characters with entirely fictional names and altered circumstances to protect patient confidentiality. When referring to my MedPsych colleagues, I use their real names and titles with great pride and affection.

Acknowledgments

THIS BOOK WOULD NOT HAVE BEEN POSSIBLE WITHOUT THE support and guidance of my remarkable MedPsych colleagues at Hasbro Children's Hospital. The steadfast support of the physicians, nurse practitioners, nurses, rehabilitative therapists, and countless others, beginning from the moment I first stepped onto the MedPsych unit, allowed me the chance to learn and grow in ways that transformed me as a pediatrician. In particular, I wish to thank the experts who read through these pages and gave me invaluable feedback. They include Dr. Diane DerMarderosian, Dr. Dan Spencer, Dr. Linda Doberstein, Dr. Mirabelle Mattar, and Dr. Fran Pingatore.

I also wish to acknowledge a deep debt of gratitude to the members of my writers' group. For the past three years I have met with fellow writers Steve Casserly, Trish Giramma, Larry Rand, Elizabeth Quincy, and Karen Lee, under the discerning guidance of Lauren Sarat. Week after week they listened carefully and responded insightfully to what I was trying to convey as I moved my work forward from a weekly installment of passionate ideas to a meaningful expression of my MedPSych experience.

I must also express my admiration and gratitude to Steven and Dawn Porter and their team at Stillwater River Publications for their professionalism and support in bringing this work to life.

And finally, thank you to my husband, Randy, for never doubting that I had something important to say.

Introduction

PEDIATRICIANS ENCOUNTER MANY TRUTHS ABOUT CHIL-
dren on a daily basis. Among those, we witness firsthand that
anxiety is a universal experience, and that children, by their very
place in nature, feel vulnerable and crave protection. We also witness
that although children and teens have feelings in abundance, they do
not always have the cognitive maturity or even the vocabulary to express
them. So it is not surprising to pediatricians when we find that children,
with their limited skills for navigating emotional storms, start experiencing their scary emotions not as feelings, but rather through their bodies.

In 2015 I accepted a position as the medical director of Hasbro Children's Hospital's Inpatient Medical/Psychiatric unit. The job was going
to be, at least in my mind, an interesting capstone to my decades-long
career in pediatrics. I would be joining a team of physicians, psychologists,
pain specialists, rehabilitation therapists, dieticians, and social workers in
developing a unique hospital program to treat adolescents with emotionally based illness—disorders that blur the lines between medical and psychiatric illness. I expected the psychological concepts that came to frame
this work to feel new and different. I also assumed I would stay in my
familiar lane, and the behavioral specialists would stay in theirs.

I had a lot to learn. At the top of that list: there were no lanes. My job description as medical director of the Inpatient program was to not only oversee and coordinate the medical treatment of our patients, but to integrate that care seamlessly with the psychiatric care. I quickly realized that on the MedPsych unit everybody played their own instruments, to their own set of notes. And each of us was responsible to each other for making sure it all came together in one fluid orchestration.

The neuroscience of emotionally based illness has been burgeoning for two decades, but this knowledge has not fully made its way out of the academic centers and into the community. MedPsych illness continues to be widely misunderstood, and is frequently met with skepticism and judgment. I welcomed the chance to apply my pediatric experience to the management of psychiatrically based disorders, but to be honest, in my previous primary care pediatric practice I often felt that validating these illnesses required a certain suspension of belief, as in, *Well let's just say this abdominal pain is real.* I was hired for the MedPsych position because of my extensive experience in pediatrics. Yet as naive as an intern stepping into a hectic intensive care unit for the first time, my first humbling lesson was how much I didn't know.

Like most general pediatricians I had spent a large amount of time with kids who tended to feel their emotions with their bodies. I'm referring to the Monday morning tummy aches, the chronic vague headaches, the unexplained nonstop cough that disappears when the child falls asleep. These symptoms come to a head because they prevent the child from going to school. It takes experience and strong communication skills to gently guide a worried family away from over-medicalizing a situation that doesn't warrant it. Pediatricians tend to be pretty good at that. Simply put, we usually recognize when a conversation is better than a CT scan. The alternative, a "let's rule out everything" mentality, is for amateurs. Ordering a long list of tests may give one the feeling of being knowledgeable and conscientious, but it is wasteful and much less effective. In fact it often makes the situation worse.

I, like my most of my pediatric colleagues, knew what steps to take to help get most school-avoidant kiddos back on track. It would involve a compassionate but committed strategy to get the child into the school building even in the face of distress. With a large dose of trust and support these strategies were often successful. But they seemed to have grown out of collective pediatric wisdom rather than science, and with little standardization. And there were always those tough cases where the child only grew more distressed and symptomatic with this process, or the parents became more agitated—even hostile—as we tried to veer from "medical" diagnoses. Things would go badly. The child's symptoms would escalate. There would be demands to see specialists.

What do I see more clearly after working on the MedPsych unit? For one thing, I now fully understand that the kids who are experiencing these emotional illnesses are actually experiencing the symptoms that go with them, even if they are not of "physical" origin. This single but critical shift in mindset is at the core of understanding emotionally driven illness.

I also understand more clearly why these kiddos and their families often resisted treatment. I marveled at, and at times grew quite frustrated, with parents who refused to see what was so clearly going on. Now I can see this as another symptom of the illness, not parental oblivion. For a school-avoidant child the emotional brain sees school as danger. Illness is the armor. The child doesn't want to be sick or even pretend to be sick. She needs to feel safe. And her eight-year-old emotional brain is telling her body that right now abdominal pain is what safety looks like. Likewise, her parents don't want to challenge their distressed child. Their instincts are shouting at them to protect her. These are the family dynamics that the illness produces and feeds on. Getting frustrated with the child or parents for not wanting to shift the focus away from a medical diagnosis is like getting angry with a pneumonia patient for having a fever.

One of the most useful lessons I learned from MedPsych work was to not debate diagnoses. Pediatricians naturally see their role, among other things, as explaining "Why I don't think this is celiac disease," or whatever other conditions have been terrifying the parents in the middle of the night. But this approach often backfires when a child's physical symptoms are actually arising from the emotional brain. For the child as well as the parents, the focus on medical illness is what is keeping the messier emotional distress at bay. When the pediatrician challenges a medical diagnosis as being unlikely it often only increases the family's agitation. What they are often hearing is that now even their own doctor doesn't believe them.

I learned a little late in my career that we don't need to disprove or argue or even discuss the accumulated medical diagnoses in this situation. We just need to set all that aside for a bit and focus on restoring the child's normal function (usually a return to school). The focus changes from challenging the family's beliefs about medical diagnoses to addressing the loss of function. Parents can usually get on board with that. If we can do that in a supportive way and at the same time help the child to connect more directly with their feelings, the illness loses its oxygen, and medical diagnoses fall away—not from being debated or disproven, but rather from becoming irrelevant.

As rich as my MedPsych experience was, it also left me with a nagging disappointment that I hadn't learned it all sooner. I realized in retrospect that for all my experience and good intentions, I had been practicing in my previous outpatient setting with one hand tied behind my back. I can see now that I was less able to help some of my more challenging kiddos because they and their parents sensed (rightly) that we—the community of healthcare providers, school personnel, and opinionated relatives—did not fully believe that the children with emotionally based physical symptoms were actually suffering those symptoms. When that happens, we instantly lose credibility.

I also see now how I was banging my head against the wall as I earnestly challenged diagnoses that just didn't make sense, pointing out parents' errors of thought with the best of intentions, as if it was a deficit of medical information that had them all sitting in my office that day. And I can see now that the defensive reactions I myself would experience in the face of hostility from a parent were born of my ignorance as to how the child's illness had actually impacted the whole family.

This is what I saw in hindsight as I gained MedPsych experience. When we fully grasp how unconscious and real emotionally based symptoms are, those skeptical voices in our heads that tell us the child is faking will disappear. Once we banish those voices, and are able to knowledgeably address the actual dynamics of the illness, the parents are more likely to align with us. They are more likely to accept psychoeducation instead of a lab slip. Even if some families remain unconvinced of the emotional component of the illness, we may at least plant a seed that could eventually make sense to them, especially if seeds are being planted consistently from doctor to doctor.

If I could go back in time this is the gap I would fill in my own previous practice. I can't do that. But what I and the growing number of pediatric providers who work in the MedPsych field can do is help bridge this wealth of knowledge from teaching centers out to the front line, to the mainstream community, to healthcare providers and educators, to parents, and most of all to all those worried little kiddos out there who are feeling way too much of their emotions through their bodies.

The need to maximize our effectiveness in diagnosing and treating emotionally driven medical issues in children and teens has never been greater. We are experiencing a pediatric mental health crisis in our country. There has been a steady rise in depression, anxiety, and suicide in children and teens over the previous decade. Pediatric centers across the country noted a further doubling of that suicide rate in children and teens between 2019 and 2020. There are solid reasons to suspect that the saturation of our children's lives with social media has played a large part in this, and social media is not going away. The emergence of the Covid pandemic, with its shutdowns and school closures, isolation and grief, has only exacerbated the crisis. Our surgeon general, Dr. Vivek Murthy, released an advisory in 2021 addressing this devastating mental health crisis in today's youth.

Suicidality is the most extreme expression of our children's angst and, as our surgeon general urged, is a call to action at every level of our society. We also need to understand what is happening below that horrifying surface of child and adolescent suicide. According to recent studies, self-reported depression and anxiety have been spreading like a quiet wildfire among our youth, fueled not only by the Covid pandemic but also by fear for their very futures. What are they reporting as their black clouds? School shootings, relentless social injustice, the crippling, dream-crushing cost of higher education, and of course the very survivability of their planet.

All of us who are tasked with the well-being of children have to be alert to this pandemic of pain. We can expect that where there is more anxiety, there will be an increasing rate of emotionally driven illness across the spectrum of severity. Our attitudes and approaches to these disorders, right down to our word choice, need to reflect an adequate understanding of their nature. Now more than ever, we need to translate that understanding into our mindsets, our conversations, and our clinical approaches.

We cannot all be neuroscientists, psychologists, and psychiatrists, but what my MedPsych experience taught me was that for the large majority of cases we don't need to be. We just need to stretch our brains a bit. It is my hope that this book will help achieve that.

CHAPTER I

A Blast from the Past

MY MEDPSYCH STORY STARTED THE FIRST DAY I STEPPED out of the elevator and onto the sixth floor of Hasbro Children's Hospital. But the other story, the one that was waiting in the background, was what this highly specialized experience would teach me about the emotionally based illnesses I had seen and treated in my previous outpatient practice. That story begins with Eleanor, who arrived at my office first thing one Monday morning flanked by two tense parents.

Eleanor had always been a healthy kid. Her parents tended to fret over her, but not in an alarming way. She had a younger brother who was generally low maintenance. He was a needed-to-be-fed-and-reminded-to-shower kind of guy. Eleanor, however, according to her mother, was a "sensitive" child who needed little supervision but typically looked to her parents to run interference for her when her world became scary.

What can be scary to an eight-year-old? A sea of strange faces in the cafeteria, "Good" on a project instead of "Excellent," a tired teacher's impatient remark. Eleanor would absorb these incidents at school and wring them out at home in the form of tearful distress which in turn evoked distress in her parents.

That is not to say that the source of a child's distress is always school. But school participation is one of the most significant markers we have for how well a child is functioning socially, emotionally, and developmentally. If marital discord or a parent's illness or a learning difference or a traumatic event are rocking the child's world, any of these could cause the child to be afraid to walk out the door in the morning and head to school. The reality in this particular therapeutic moment is that from a pediatrician's viewpoint, we have no idea what is causing Eleanor's distress. And, at least for the moment, we don't need to. We need to restore function. That means we need to get her back into school.

As is often the case with worried parents, Eleanor's mother and father found themselves running interference for her more and more frequently at school. Operating within their own mix of parental instincts and personality types, they had trouble tolerating distress in their child, and were inclined to try and fix the problem themselves rather than hold Eleanor's hand through it. Most of us can relate to this inclination on some level. It is tempting for all of us to try and iron out the wrinkles in our children's lives. We need to understand and have compassion for the families that find themselves in these messy situations.

Pediatricians typically offer kindness and compassion by the truckload. But as I was to learn through my MedPsych experience, a truckload of good intentions is not enough. Our kindness and compassion need to be smart too.

Over the previous months a pattern had begun to emerge with Eleanor. She was generally okay over weekends and school vacations, but her symptoms flared on school days. Sunday nights and Monday mornings were the worst. When she was in school she was going to the nurse's office every day.

School absenteeism is a giant red flag for pediatricians. School attendance frames important developmental functions for most children. When an unexplained symptom consistently keeps a child out of school it needs our attention. As I learned in the office that day, my little friend Eleanor was missing way too much school—five days just in the past two weeks for unexplained symptoms.

If Eleanor had a stomachache that prevented her from finishing breakfast that morning, but she insisted on going to school anyway because she didn't want to miss play practice, then I would have been less focused on emotionally driven symptoms at that visit. Why? Because she doesn't appear to be avoiding anything. The symptoms are not keeping her from age-appropriate tasks like going to school. It's likely just a minor kerfuffle in her abdomen. If a child's physical complaint does not lead to a loss of function, like school attendance, then we are much less inclined to focus on emotional causes.

But this is clearly not the case with Eleanor. Her symptoms escalate the closer she gets to those giant front doors of that giant brick building. Just as importantly, the symptoms ease when she is able to avoid that experience, like on weekends. A pediatrician will still screen for medical issues in this situation, mostly by history and physical exam, but it becomes clear from Eleanor's story that we needed to focus on the emotional factors. Addressing the trembling elephant in the room cannot wait until we have ruled out every possible "physical" cause.

Eleanor didn't know why school was scary. In fact, she didn't fully realize that it was scaring her. But her unconscious emotions, in a frantic display of strength, were working overtime to keep her home, signaling to her tummy that it hurt in a way that made her feel desperate and tearful and in need of protection. All this misleading input assaulting Eleanor's consciousness translated to a very convincing picture of someone who should indeed stay home from school.

Emotionally driven illnesses have tendrils especially designed to reach out and grab the adults in this situation—and not just the parents. Eleanor typically did all her work to perfection, and continued to do so at home. She frequently expressed how much she loved school and hated to miss it. Her teachers adored her and made every effort to accommodate her by providing home assignments along with lots of sympathy and understanding. One teacher even stopped by the house with get-well cards from her classmates.

Meanwhile, as is typical school policy, the principal assured Eleanor's family that as long as she got a doctor's note to cover each of the absences, they would be "excused." This is where softhearted educators, as well as pediatricians such as myself, are in danger of becoming part of the problem. The line between compassion and enabling can at times be very thin. If we're not vigilant, we too can catch this contagious illness as easily as we get a cold from a kiddo who coughs in our face.

One of the child psychiatrists at Hasbro often referred to these compassion-based accommodations as "errors of kindness." We've all been there. Eleanor's illness, by its very nature, evokes sympathy—especially from kind people.

For every misfired signal her emotional brain is sending out to the rest of her body, causing her to experience pain where there is no pathology, Eleanor's cognitive brain is working overtime to make sense of this decoy:

I love school, I hate being too sick to go. But I can't go. I just can't. I'm in too much pain.

What kind of monster wouldn't want to try and make her day a little easier? Errors of kindness.

As Eleanor's story continued to unfold, it became clear that everyone in the family has been affected by this illness. Mom had called in sick for work again that morning, with a mixture of anxiety and frustration. She was spending down her bank of goodwill from coworkers. Eleanor's brother chased the school bus down the street that morning, having missed breakfast and forgotten his lunch. And not daring to complain.

Can't you see your sister is not feeling well?

Dad had been growing impatient, suggesting they were coddling Eleanor too much, and there's a bit of friction in the air about that.

"My husband thinks you should just 'tough everything out,'" Mom said with annoyance, looking at me as if Dad wasn't right there in the room.

The parents were both sort of right and they were both sort of wrong. They both absolutely wanted to do the right thing. They just didn't see what that was yet. The solutions are too counterintuitive. And little brother? From what the parents told me he was just keeping his head down, sending out occasional unwelcome signals of frustration with his sister.

The family came to my office that Monday morning not only for a doctor's excuse, but also with a growing list of diagnoses the parents thought we should explore. Eleanor sat very still on the exam table as I talked with her parents, chewing on her lip a bit and occasionally pushing her hair away from her face as she watched her mother answer my questions. She glanced at me only briefly now and then, looking down when I tried to include her in the conversation, shrugging her shoulders and murmuring her responses. It was noteworthy that Eleanor appeared as worried about this office visit as her parents appeared about her health. Nobody wanted to talk about feelings. Avoidance is anxiety's favorite dance partner, and with all my questions about her feelings Eleanor was starting to get the message that I was about to cut in.

To be clear, Eleanor had little inkling as to why this visit was worrying her. To her, the symptoms were very real. If she could have identified what was really frightening her—the typical social and academic speed bumps of school mixed in perhaps with a bit of separation anxiety—she wouldn't have belly pain to begin with. But Eleanor is lingering, uncertain, at a developmental crossroad. The Big World outside, with its everyday challenges to our identity, our egos, and our sense of safety, was too overwhelming for this little girl at this particular moment in her maturation for her to deal with the anxiety directly. Yet she also understood that she was expected to go to school, and she really wanted to be the good girl that everyone thought she was. The end result was recurring unexplained belly pain and missed school, and it's as common in childhood as scraped knees.

How Eleanor and her family fared depended on many things. There are of course the usual factors, like genetics and personality style. Her course would also be affected by her parents' attitudes and how much they trusted me, as well as any other stressors that were currently swimming around her family. And it would certainly be shaped to a very significant degree by the mindset and biases of her medical providers.

That would be me of course, long before I ever heard the term "Med-Psych illness."

CHAPTER 2

Common Ground

I ARRIVED FOR MY INTERVIEW AT HASBRO CHILDREN'S HOSPI-
tal feeling immediately out of place in the unfamiliar and highly
specialized setting of the MedPsych unit. Even my interview out-
fit—a skirt and the pointiest shoes I had worn in years—underscored
the strangeness of the situation. I had three decades of pediatric practice
under my belt. At a time when my colleagues were eyeing their 401(k)
s with an eye toward retirement I was seriously contemplating a major
shift in the type of medicine I practiced, leaving my comfort zone to
start something very new.

A few weeks previously, scrolling through a copy of the Rhode Island
Medical Society's monthly bulletin, I happened to spot a job posting
squeezed into a small box on the first page. Prior to that sighting my
primary career goal was to negotiate a lighter call schedule. I felt I had
earned the right to ease up a little. My pediatric experience up to that
point was pretty typical corduroys-and-clogs pediatrics. Casual. Flexi-
ble. Occasional conflict but mostly warm and satisfying work. The big-
gest strain was usually fatigue, not the emotional content of the room.

Then somehow this small, unassuming notice in the Rhode Island Medical Society's newsletter pulled me in, like a gravitational force from an unfamiliar mass up in Providence. I loosened my footing on all the familiar ground that had been supporting me, as well as any hope of a lightened workload, and succumbed to a pull into the unknown

I was escorted on to the MedPsych unit through two sets of locked doors. The nurse manager, Jen, explained as we passed through that the security was for patients' safety. The locked doors meant that the patients had more freedom to move around on the unit and engage with others without overbearing restrictions. To me, the heavy clunk of the locks resetting in our wake made me feel a sense of danger, not safety or freedom. My first gut feeling on the MedPsych unit was that this was not for me.

As we crossed the unit we passed a dozen or so teenagers sitting in cushy sofas and chairs in a common area. Some looked up curiously as we walked by, others seemed indifferent, and a few sat by themselves. It looked like they could have been hanging out in a lounge at school. I wondered how these young people felt about this closing off from the world. I hadn't grasped yet that each of them had already removed themselves emotionally and physically from the world they were designed for. This unit would actually be their reentry point.

I was led to the conference room to join morning rounds and was immediately struck by the large number of staff and providers sitting around a couple of large tables that had been pushed together. A picture window as long as the room served as backdrop. I was offered a seat at one end, and fumbled to pull the chair out from the table, not expecting it to be so heavy.

"All the chairs here are weighted," smiled the woman in the next chair. "Hi, I'm Sarah O. by the way."

She was a social worker it turned out—one of several in the room. My escort Jen added, in that matter-of-fact way that career nurses have mastered, "That's so they're too heavy to be thrown." I sat down in the chair about two feet from the table edge to avoid any further struggle with furniture in front of this audience. Jen went on to explain to the group who I was and why I was there.

I felt dizzied by the fifteen or so staff faces all looking at me with interest now. The psychiatry director, Dan Spencer, who I had interviewed with earlier that day, was leading the daily rounds. He suggested the team go around the table and tell me their names and what their roles were. Names (except Sarah O.'s) got lost in the ether. What had my full attention was the remarkable variety of disciplines gathered in one room. Psychiatrists, psychologists, social workers, nurses, mental health workers, dieticians and rehab therapists, all sitting around a table together, all actively participating, in a mostly orderly fashion. This was a luxury I had never encountered before. The conversation quickly got back to business. The process surprised me.

Any rounds I had ever participated in involved moving like a rugby scrum from room to room, exchanging rapid-fire data about the patient of the moment. This was so different. A nurse, seated at the head of the table, was describing a seizure-like event that had happened the night before, and why it did not seem to the staff to be consistent with an epileptic convulsion. I knew of this kind of episode as the commonly used term "pseudoseizure," but this group used the more appropriate term, "nonepileptic seizure." As I would soon come to better understand, there was nothing "pseudo" about such an episode.

The mental health worker (MHW)—one of the staff that ran the day-to-day activities on the unit—talked about what this patient's goals were for the day, and how she wanted to talk to her doctors about being allowed to have time off the unit. This started a very detailed back-and-forth between the MHW and the psychologist, another Sarah, about what criteria the patient had to meet to be able to do that. The pediatrician shared past EEG results, another social worker updated the team on her meeting with the parents, and Dan shared his own thoughts on the behavior plan and talked about adjusting meds. The nutritionist noted that the patient seemed a bit underweight, and recommended we monitor her eating behaviors on the unit. Discussion, discussion, and more discussion. Sixteen patients were discussed in one and a half hours, and nobody left their seat.

I sat there, wordless, my neck swiveling back and forth between team members, self-conscious about my stupid chair being two feet from the table that everyone else was pulled up to, wondering how in the world all this talk translated into any kind of cohesive treatment. And how in the world an outpatient primary care pediatrician like me could fit in, much less take a leadership role.

It was like a breath of fresh air to head out to the unit again, moving in and around the teenagers, hearing their voices, watching them participate in a community meeting. It turned out to be the patients themselves that made sense out of all this for me that day. Here was the common ground. A sullen guy who one minute was snarling and indignant about the ban on personal electronic devices turned to me just moments later to tell me with a warm smile how much he liked my earrings. An emaciated older teen got up from her seat and put her arms around another patient who had begun to cry. A mental health worker masterfully coaxed a shy wisp of a girl to tell us about her dog. I heard her say, just above a whisper, that it was a lab, and then she said its name but I couldn't make it out. All those young pairs of ears in the room did, though, and gushed or overtalked or smiled in appreciation.

My breathing slowed, my eyes and ears tuned in, my brain took notes. I put aside for a moment the Tower of Babel that was morning rounds. There would be time to adjust to that. The patients pulled me back into who I was and why I was there.

The sullen guy with the acne and the fabulous taste in earrings—I'd start him on acne treatment right away. There is no better way to earn the trust and improve the mood of a teen than improving their acne. That thin girl, I'd want to see what nutritional and metabolic studies had been done, and I might check in with the Eating Disorder team about her—a luxury I certainly didn't have at my fingertips outside of this hospital. I would know what these kids needed from me. And if what they needed was something other than a pediatrician, I would know that too. Scanning the room, I was reminded of just how much I had learned about patients and families over the previous decades, and I began to get a glimmer of how I could fold that into all the nuanced treatment modalities that had been discussed in rounds.

What I did not yet grasp was that in return I would be learning more from my MedPsych colleagues and patients in the next few years than I would have ever thought possible. I could not yet imagine how much I would come to love this place and this work, or how much this Med-Psych work would transform me. Teaming up with the likes of Dan and Sarah O. and Sarah no-last-initial-yet, with those seasoned nurses and skilled mental health workers, and all those other folks whose names and roles I would eventually sort out, I would become the most complete pediatrician I had ever been.

CHAPTER 3

Welcome to Rhode Island

A T FIRST GLANCE, ELEANOR MIGHT SEEM TO HAVE VERY little in common with the severely compromised adolescents that we treated on the MedPsych unit. This distinction is typical of how doctors learn. The months of training I spent in a highly specialized neonatal intensive care unit, taking care of extremely fragile preemies, taught me many important principles about the sick infants I would someday see in my primary care practice. I was not too surprised when I realized that working with severe emotionally driven illness in the MedPsych unit taught me many basic principles that, in retrospect, would have made me more effective in treating the worried little Eleanors as well.

One of my earliest MedPsych lessons involved Mike, a thirteen-year-old who was diagnosed with nonepileptic seizures or NES.

Over the preceding year Mike had intermittent spells of falling to the floor, writhing, and shaking while seemingly going in and out of consciousness. The episodes started occurring at school, and then began happening at home as well. He had an extensive workup at a prestigious children's hospital in California without any abnormal findings. His many EEGs during these episodes showed a normal pattern of electrical discharge. Perhaps even more significant is that the abnormal bilateral movements Mike exhibited during these episodes—mostly erratic shakiness and flailing—were not consistent with the specific kinds of jerks and stiffening seen in a generalized seizure. The conclusion, after extensive blood tests, two spinal taps, and lots of brain imaging, from specialist after specialist, was that there was no evidence of epilepsy. There was no evidence of any neurologic impairments.

And yet the events kept happening, and the more the doctors became convinced that Mike did not have a neurological disorder, the worse he got. He was ultimately diagnosed with a functional neurologic disorder or FND. FND has been more commonly referred to as conversion disorder in the past. It refers to emotionally driven illness that presents as a neurologic condition, such as seizures—what Mike was suffering—or other neurologic deficits like paralysis or sensory malfunction.

The family, not surprisingly, was skeptical of this consensus. They had witnessed many of these spells and were terrified by them. There was no way their son was "faking" this. By the time Mike was referred to our MedPsych unit, he had been unable to attend school at all for many months. The more the doctors recommended returning to school, the more prolonged and profound the episodes became. As is often the case with MedPsych illness, challenging the conviction that this was a "structural" or "anatomic" or "medical" problem in his brain, and suggesting it was an emotional one, only escalated his symptoms. His illness unconsciously adjusted in order to squash any doubt about just how medically sick he was.

As a last resort, Mike and his family agreed to treatment in our program. They flew across the country and nervously passed through our locked doors. It was late by the time they arrived. Rhode Island is many wonderful things, but it is not California. Especially in November. It was cold and dark outside, and it had begun to rain. They all looked dazed and horrified. It was slowly dawning on them that they had made a terrible mistake. The nurses and mental health workers knew to expect this, and managed to keep them all calm and occupied with the business of settling in. I kept my own introduction friendly and brief. The rattled, exhausted parents were instructed on how to get to the Ronald McDonald House and escorted off the unit. The first family meeting with Mike's doctors would be in the morning.

Twelve hours later the team was gathered in a conference room on the unit to meet with Mike's parents. Mike would be invited to join a little later. After introductions were made, we invited them to tell us Mike's story in their own words, starting with a description of what Mike was like before his illness. They would use the past tense of course, but to those of us sitting around the table listening, it was all about the future. We were gathering clues about the place we hoped to bring Mike back to. Mike's parents recognized that the spells did indeed correlate with other things that were going on in their lives. If the parents were arguing, or a friend invited him to a party, or a doctor recommended that he be transitioned back into school, the episodes would intensify. His attempts to return frequently ended in a call to 911. The parents of course were quite distressed when the convulsions occurred in their presence—running to his side, making sure he was breathing, stroking his hair, getting him a pillow. They bought a hospital bed with padding to keep him from hurting himself. They were grateful for his sake that he never lost bowel or bladder control during these events, and never incurred any significant injury. The school was hesitant to have him return, as this usually precipitated a call to 911 before the day was out.

Mom quit her job to stay home with Mike even though that presented financial hardship. Mike's growing needs became the center of her life. Dad was feeling powerless and marginalized. He was losing patience with the endless parade of doctors who could not figure out what was wrong. Mike's twin sister, who had never caused her parents a bit of worry, just got suspended for bringing alcohol to school.

We had all the factual parts of this information before we accepted Mike to the program, before he ever walked onto our unit. We had pored through hundreds of pages of medical records, and had many phone calls with the patient and family, as well as with many of his doctors. But this first meeting was about so much more. As in the treatment of any other medical condition, you have to first listen to the patient's story, whether it is told by the child or the parent. In pediatrics, it is often critical to hear the family's story as well. We know that parents are usually the experts when it comes to their child. In our family meeting we paid special attention to all the ways a parent knows their child, what their family belief systems were, what they valued and how they all related to each other.

The team was in agreement that Mike's case illustrated the cardinal features of MedPsych illness. I would learn over the coming years that these features were quite consistent whether a patient was presenting with seizures, chronic pain, or the inability to walk. Like the child with new onset diabetes who presents with excessive thirst and urination, MedPsych disorders also present in a typical pattern. But unlike diabetes, where the telltale signs are bouncing around the child's body, the telltale signs of MedPsych disorders are bouncing around the child's life.

First, there is always a significant loss of function, regardless of the presenting symptoms. For most children the primary way this manifests is the inability to attend school and the associated social isolation, in the absence of medical findings. In Mike's case this functional loss was the result of frequent convulsive-type behaviors.

Secondly, there is resistance to treatment. The more reassuring the medical evaluations were, and the more the diagnosis of epilepsy was challenged, the more dramatic and debilitating Mike's symptoms became. This makes sense once the dynamics of the illness are understood. His unconscious emotional brain was being backed into a corner and working overtime to maintain the protective shield that the convulsions had been providing. The emotional brain, through misfired signals out to the body, was calling the shots. Getting "better" was not a safe option.

Thirdly, the illness infects the whole family. MedPsych illness by its very nature confuses and terrifies parents. As my colleagues taught me, if there was an intuitive way for parents to get out of this mess on their own, there would be no need for MedPsych treatment. Mike's parents were doing everything thing in their power to ease his distress and keep him safe, at the expense of their own wellbeing and that of their marriage, their finances, and even the other siblings. I came to understand how counterintuitive the management of emotionally based illness was for parents. Over time I felt myself becoming less frustrated by a mom who insisted we let her son lie in bed all day, less judgmental about a dad who angrily insisted that his daughter not go to group therapy anymore because she had nothing in common with all those other kids in there. I would also check in about the siblings now and then. When possible, we would arrange for them to come to a few family therapy sessions. They were suffering too.

And lastly, kind people did everything they could to accommodate Mike through this illness. His teachers sent schoolwork home covered in cheery post-it notes. His classmates sent sympathetic cards that reinforced how brave he was in the face of this mysterious illness. His coach was holding a place for him on the soccer team, even though he missed tryouts. One of the child psychiatrists referred to this common reaction as "errors of kindness." Everyone was working very hard to minimize the toll this illness had taken on Mike's life. But in a toxic, and completely unintended way, these accommodations only provided more oxygen to the illness.

Loss of function, treatment resistance, altered family dynamics, and accommodation are universal features of emotionally driven illness, whether the physical symptom is a tummy ache, a convulsion, or paralysis. If we see, look for, and identify these features in a child with unexplained medical complaints then we need to put emotionally based illness front and center on our diagnostic list.

This is the roadmap that led us to the diagnosis of emotionally driven disorders, and more specifically, to Mike's nonepileptic convulsions. It was the very same road map that unfolded when Eleanor and her family showed up in my office. I had a pretty good sense of where we needed to go back then, but I wasn't using a map. I didn't even know there was one. If I had, then treatment would have been better directed and in many cases more effective.

Unfortunately, most of the patients that were admitted to our program had, like Mike, been bouncing around the world of medical specialists for a couple of years before being referred to us. I could tell as I pored through the copious medical records that many of these highly skilled specialists—including those who realized this was emotionally based illness—were also driving around without a MedPsych map. In a story that we heard over and over again, relentless doctor shopping dovetailed with a steady escalation of functional loss, deepening treatment resistance, altered family dynamics, and a world of accommodations. Precious time was wasted. Over-medicalization was matched by a predictable worsening of illness. Referral to the MedPsych unit was presented as a last resort.

There were a lot of us at the table in that first family meeting. The core of Mike's team was a psychiatrist, a psychologist, a pediatrician, a nurse, and a mental health worker. Also at the team core were Mike and his parents. We emphasized right from the first long-distance phone call that they all needed to be active participants within the treatment team. That meant the parents needed to be here in Rhode Island with Mike to participate in family therapy. No decisions would be made without their input.

Other disciplines were included in family meetings according to need. In Mike's case a physical therapist was present to weigh in on therapies that could help with Mike's frequent headaches and his dizziness. A dietician was there to explain her role in addressing Mike's recent weight loss and dietary restrictions. As Mike's treatment progressed, our Pain/Palliative Care team would be there to reassess his medications and to offer integrative coping skills and other modalities such as massage and yoga.

The lead psychologist, Sarah Hagin, often led the first family meeting, with the rest of us called upon to add to or reinforce the information and the plan, and underscore the multidisciplinary nature of this integrative approach. And, critically, we were all there to ensure that the providers were communicating with each other and were aligned with each other in the therapeutic messaging. Real-time integrative care would define one of the major differences between our program and the parade of specialists' care that Mike's family had sought as outpatients.

What did these terrified parents want to tell us about their son at the family meeting? They focused on the convulsions, as this was the most tangible aspect of the illness and what worried them the most. They discussed their fear that a serious medical diagnosis was getting missed. And they expressed their dismay at all the rules and restrictions on the unit. Even though we go to great lengths prior to admission to explain what both our facility and our clinical approach look like, families were usually pretty freaked out by the reality of it all once they arrived. No amount of phone calls can convey the feeling of walking through a series of locked doors for the first time, or arranging yourselves on chairs designed to be too heavy to throw. I could vouch for that.

When we met MedPsych parents for the first time they were lost in a dark cave. What I learned from my colleagues was to offer them a flashlight before I handed them the map. Understanding the true nature of emotionally based illness allows a pediatrician to do just that. Whether I was meeting a trembling little girl as an outpatient or surly Mike in the hospital, I needed to find out where they all were and start out by validating their experiences. I needed to educate them on emotionally based illness without debating or dismissing diagnoses. That was how I could help show them the way home.

CHAPTER 4

Tears

PEDIATRICIANS AND PARENTS CAN USUALLY GET A QUICK handle on the tummy aches that cry out for staying home from school. Even our grandmothers had that partly figured out. Their no-nonsense unless-you're-dying-you're-going-to-school approach featured at least one part of effective treatment: restore function. But we also understand now that emotional support is just as critical as restoring function. We need to teach children how to name and connect with their feelings, and we need to proceed stepwise rather than sink or swim, so as not to overwhelm a child's fledgling coping mechanisms.

What I learned from the extreme level of symptoms that we treated in our MedPsych program was that, like any other aspect of medical treatment, the physician has to understand the nature of the illness if she is going to be effective. This applies to emotionally driven illness just as it would to diabetes or malaria. It applies to Eleanor as much as to it does to Mike. And for most of us it requires a cognitive shift that can be as challenging as it is nuanced. I learned and came to fully accept as I worked alongside psychiatrists and psychologists that the experience of emotionally driven symptoms was as real as a toothache. The patients in my care were not faking. Eleanor was not faking. I now know this to be true. But it still can be a hard sell to others, especially worried parents.

"You're telling me there's nothing medically wrong with him but he's not faking?"

The common human experience of emotional crying—tearfulness—can help our cognitive centers understand our emotional brain a little better.

A few years back when I was in New York City for a pediatric conference, I treated myself to a ticket to *Les Miserables* on Broadway. It was a packed theater, and I was sitting shoulder to shoulder with total strangers. There were several points in the show where I felt so emotional that a swelling sensation arose in my throat and I strained to control the quivering facial expressions that I knew would be followed by tears. I felt embarrassed to be crying over actors on a stage, and in the presence of strangers no less. But when the character Jean Valjean began to sing "Bring Him Home," my self-control cracked. I sat there helplessly, trying to stifle my sniffles, wiping my eyes as subtly as I could, swallowing quietly until the pressure in my throat abated.

Emotional crying is not a disorder, and in fact scientists speculate that we can probably trace its evolutionary purpose to providing nonverbal infant animals, including humans, with a means of communicating distress. Unless you are an actor of the caliber of Meryl Streep you probably cannot cry on demand. And once you've started crying, you are likely unable to will it to stop. Your emotional brain is in the driver's seat. Cognitive function, scrambling to reassure us—*"These are actors on a stage. None of this is actually happening"*—has been pushed aside.

Crying is a phenomenon we all readily, unquestionably, accept as fact. Nobody sitting near me in the theater that night would have wondered if I was faking my tears or having an allergic reaction to sad songs. It would be obvious to everyone that my very intangible emotions produced a very tangible, unwanted, involuntary result: tears. To put it another way, no reasonable person observing me in that *Les this* moment would think I must have a medical condition, or I must be using some trickery, because there's no way just a thought or feeling could produce that very physical display of salt water and mucus.

Even brain scientists do not yet have a complete understanding of the neurochemical pathways that can turn the emotional experience of hearing a sad song into an overflow of eye water, facial muscle contractions, and painful swallowing. And yet we all know and accept that it happens all the time. What *do* neuroscientists know about emotional crying? They know it involves a highly complex system of neurotransmitters and lots of specialized proteins. When these impossible-to-pronounce substances are secreted by the brain's emotional centers they stimulate and coordinate sites throughout the brain. Many of these pathways have been identified. But some remain only hopeful dotted lines on paper. We know they are there. They just haven't fully revealed themselves to us. Yet.

These highways of emotion reach out across the primitive limbic brain, from the amygdala to locations throughout the cortex, including the "neuromatrix"—the region of the cortex which processes how we experience pain. Picture, if you can, a detailed, multicolored subway map of New York City, where half the station stops and transfer points are named in Latin and the other half haven't been named yet. Why should we believe that a passenger riding underground in the dark can predictably get to a specific and relatively remote destination on this path? We can't see how it happens. It's dark down there. Yet we know where we started and we're pretty sure about where we'll end up.

The brain mapping that we are discerning today will lead us someday to a fuller understanding about emotionally driven illnesses like functional neurologic disorder (previously known as conversion disorder) and somatic symptom disorder. Someday we will be able to explain to Eleanor's parents just how her school-related anxiety got translated by her brain into physical pain. But all we can say right now is that the underground trip can and does happen. The pathways are there—as surely as the better-understood physiologic pathways that cause our heart rate to go up when we're frightened, or make our stomachs churn before a big test.

We don't want to equate a normal bodily function like emotional crying with the unhealthy processes found in MedPsych disorders, but we must hold on to this mindset with all our cognitive might: The emotional brain can and does relay signals through the central nervous system to direct (or misdirect) our physiology in ways that are out of our direct consciousness or control. It can produce harmless physical "symptoms" like tears in a healthy theater-goer. It can produce ulcers in a highly functional air traffic controller. In these cases our cognitive brains have not been overshadowed. The air traffic controller knows why he has an ulcer. We keep doing what we feel we are supposed to be doing with our lives despite these observable effects of sadness or stress on our bodies. We remain *functional*. This is not MedPsych illness.

In contrast, with MedPsych illnesses like Mike's nonepileptic seizures, or Eleanor's abdominal pain, the signals coming out of the emotional brain override cognitive functions. Mike does not connect his convulsions with any stress or anxiety. In fact he is adamant that there is no connection. He believes he has epilepsy. The same disconnect holds for Eleanor, on a much milder level of dysfunction. Her anxiety is also being deflected to bodily distress. She also is experiencing her anxiety in a disguised form—not as an emotion, but as abdominal pain that is designed to prevent her from having to experience overwhelming anxiety.

Even those of us who might have slept through high school biology have a pretty good understanding that too much stress is unhealthy. We can accept that through a variety of fight or flight adaptations stress can cause a cascade of neurochemical responses that produce a measurable pathological condition such as high blood pressure, or a tension headache, or intestinal rebellion. And most of us can then access our cognitive brain to identify the source of the stress, and take steps to manage it as best we can, like signing up for a yoga class or cutting back on our hours at work. This is what most of us understand as the "mind-body connection."

As we can see with Mike and Eleanor, understanding MedPsych illness stretches our cognitive efforts further. We need to understand that little Eleanor's abdominal pain is not simply a matter of anxiety causing increased gastric acid, or stress hormones causing her bowels to be overactive—even if those things are also actually happening to some degree. Eleanor is having abdominal pain because her emotional brain is sending misleading signals out to her healthy abdomen that it actually, really hurts. It hurts as much as a phantom limb pain. It hurts as much as a sprained ankle. Her brain is tricking her in to this to protect her from a daunting amount of emotional distress. She is feeling abdominal pain so that she doesn't have to experience emotional pain.

Returning to that subway map of New York City, as we come to understand the mechanism of Eleanor's illness we can help Eleanor make a fairly simple transfer to get her the heck out of Queens and over to where she was originally headed, the Central Park Zoo. At this point we don't need to know a lot of details about how Eleanor got lost. We just need to get her back to Penn Station and take it from there. Eleanor won't want to get back on that train again, and will need some significant hand holding. But once we get her aboveground and over to the zoo she will experience how manageable—and fun—the excursion is. She'll be okay, and in better shape to understand how she got derailed in the first place. Restoring function (getting her to the zoo), not diagnosing how or why she got lost, is the first giant step to recovery.

For our Inpatient MedPsych patients the illness is more embedded and the trip is more complicated. We're going to actually have to pull up train tracks, switch relay points, get off at every stop, wait for the next train, and get on again. Patients like Mike will be arguing with us the whole time, and his illness will urge him to sabotage all of our efforts. Meanwhile his parents will be freaking out because the air conditioning failed on the train and it's a breathless ninety-eight-degree day. They will decide by day three of the admission that we have no idea what we are doing. The entire treatment team in fact will be sweating and having our own moments of doubts and conflict as we experience a lot of treatment resistance and negative feedback. We will have to manage ourselves as much as the patient and families have to manage their reactions.

The emphasis on restoring function—getting to the zoo—without waiting for the "how did we get so lost" issues to be addressed is the basis of traditional pediatric management of school-related anxiety.

Pediatricians, please take a bow.

MedPsych principles take it further: Eleanor wasn't trying to get lost. It just happened, without her realizing it. And it was scary. And the road to recovery—getting back on that subway—was even scarier. What both Mike and Eleanor need is healthcare providers who understand that their symptoms, whether convulsions or minor abdominal pain, are quite real, and that they originate from emotional pain that is deflected to a more "acceptable" site in the body. These kiddos need providers that understand these patients are largely unaware of the emotional issues hiding behind the symptoms.

This is the drumbeat we must heed as our patients ride around in the dark:

They are not faking.
They are truly lost.
They are experiencing what they say they are experiencing.

If a medical provider is not fully convinced of all this, and is therefore unable to convey this understanding in a convincing way, they will miss the opportunity to fully address the illness. The patient will hear the low frequency message that the doctor doesn't really believe them. The parents may feel that their concerns were dismissed, and remain unconvinced that this is not a mysterious "medical" illness. They might doctor shop for more testing, more opinions. The pediatrician, facing a family that seems so stuck in their beliefs, will often be diverted into further workups and useless debates about medical diagnoses, not fully grasping why there is all this resistance.

When the pediatrician understands the emotional forces within the illness, and can truthfully validate the symptoms, she is much more likely to align with the family rather than further inflame the illness. She can provide psychoeducation that will make sense to the parents or, at the very least, plant a seed in their minds.

The severe functional deficits we see in Mike and others on the Inpatient MedPsych unit magnify the therapeutic challenges. These patients come to the program with debilitating pain syndromes, extreme motor deficits, unexplained convulsions, and all kinds of other functional issues like inability to see or to speak or to swallow. They are deficits that have no structural basis or medical explanation beyond the misfired messages the body is receiving from the emotional brain. These kiddos truly see no connection between their emotions and their physical symptoms. Accepting the diagnosis and treatment approach for MedPsych illness presents a huge leap of faith for most patients and their families, who naturally can't help but wonder what terrible conditions we are missing as we chase down an emotional trigger.

The journey from diagnosis to recovery for these patients is as emotionally and physically complicated as the array of neurochemical pathways crisscrossing the brain's subway map to produce my very real tears of grief in response to a beautiful song. One could imagine how the tears I cried in the theater are in keeping with an evolutionary adaptation for humans to connect with each other, understand each other's suffering, and signal a need for support from others. One can imagine they serve the same purpose for Mike on the MedPsych unit. They are hidden tears of anger and pain and hopelessness in patients who are suffering in the loneliest way possible—from ailments that don't actually seem to exist. As the character Jean Valjean sang so movingly in *Les Mis*:

"Bring him peace, Bring him joy, He is young, He is only a boy."

CHAPTER 5

A Sense of Humors

Y FIRST CHALLENGE IN DEALING WITH MEDPSYCH ILL-
ness involved understanding its true nature. The next and
equally challenging task was how to explain this to families.
Whether we are talking with little Eleanor's family in a cheery pediatric
office with rainbow murals on the wall, or meeting with Mike's family
in a sparse conference room on the top floor of Hasbro Children's Hospital, word choice matters. Unfortunately, the common everyday language we use to communicate with our patients about these illnesses
can feel as out of date as a discussion of Aristotle's bodily humors.

"Well Mike, your yellow bile is off the charts this morning. Let's
settle you down with some fresh air and cucumbers."

To be fair, Aristotle's concept of bodily humors was quite a step forward in medical history. His theory moved us from viewing illness as a
supernatural event to a natural one. In turn, advancing the theory as to
how ailments developed guided the use of targeted treatments. Advice
for improving one's diet and environment replaced sacrificial offerings
to the gods.

Today we take precise medical language for granted. We have the luxury of choice, discussing most medical conditions with either simple, clear words or quite complex terminology, depending on who we are talking to.

Consider a family's confusion when we recommend diet and exercise for an obese child with type 2 diabetes.

"But Doctor that doesn't make sense. First of all, he's so sensitive about his weight. We don't want to bring attention to it. And he is unable to lose weight no matter how hard he tries. He gets so discouraged. He is sad, doctor. The last thing we want to tell him is he can't eat the food he likes. And exercise? He's tired all the time. He gets out of breath just going upstairs. Exercise seems like the worst possible thing for him right now."

The family is not being illogical or untruthful. They certainly are not uncaring. They just don't fully understand the mechanism of illness, and want to alleviate the child's distress, not make things harder by emphasizing lifestyle changes.

So, with a combination of facts and imagery, we may start a discussion with a family in this way:

"Type 2 diabetes is caused by too much sugar in the blood. We know it is often linked to obesity, which in turn alters the body's metabolism. The elevated sugar levels are due largely to excessive calorie intake and a resistance of the body's cells to insulin. The body's regulatory capabilities have been overtaxed. The cells' ability to manage sugar has been exhausted. But we can reverse some of this and bring his blood sugar under control."

These words only skim the surface of our current understanding of diabetes. Get an endocrinologist, an immunologist, and a geneticist in the same room and you'll think they're speaking Klingon. But whether we are speaking in simple language to a bewildered family about their child, or attending a specialized medical conference, precision in our language is what leads not only to a shared understanding of the illness but also, very importantly, to the rationale for treatment.

Unfortunately, when it comes to emotionally driven illness our spoken language often seems inadequate, even obsolete, relative to the science. When all eyes in that first family meeting turned to me to address Mike's previous medical workup and how that fit into the whole picture, I was feeling a bit like I was back in ninth-grade French class:

"*J'allez au ...*bathroom?"

I could not remember the word for bathroom or how to put it in the form of a question so my voice went up at the end to indicate that.

"*Aux toilettes*," Sister Géneviève responded.

Hmm. Was that a yes or a no?

The language barriers were no less daunting in Mike's family meeting, and although Sister Géneviève was, thankfully, not in the room, a small army of other specialists were very much present. As long as I didn't say something potentially harmful, my colleagues would patiently allow me to stumble through the awkward language, saving their feedback for later. They knew the minefield well, and understood that I was very new.

I was in my element as I got started. I talked about the medical evidence that this was not epilepsy, I was very careful *not* to say things like "Well he doesn't *actually* have a seizure disorder." I avoided saying this not out of a need for diplomacy, but because I now recognized that he was absolutely having convulsions that were out of his conscious control. Conviction is a much better messenger than diplomacy. Families absolutely hear the difference. They may not yet be as convinced as we are about our emotionally based diagnosis, but they sense we're not trying to humor them or dismiss them or claim the higher ground with a barrage of medical facts.

A month earlier, on my first day on the MedPsych unit, I observed these family meetings silently, and was surprised that the team wasn't pushing back more when parents were insisting that everyone was missing a medical diagnosis. I thought this was an exercise in letting families think what they wanted to think until we could show them results—a sort of stalling technique to give us a chance to do our thing and watch the child improve. But by the time Mike, looking shriveled and afraid, sat across the table from me a month later, I realized that what we were actually doing was acknowledging the reality of Mike's experience, and meeting the family, honestly and sincerely, where they were.

What was I being tasked with now that I was an active participant in the family meeting?

First, the family needed to be listened to. I had a lot of knowledge to share, and had sifted through hundreds of pages of Mike's medical records, but the parents knew their child best. They had been through quite an ordeal, including two years of extensive medical evaluations—a process that only reinforced the mindset that their son had a serious medical illness that no one could figure out. This paradox kept resurfacing in MedPsych stories over the years. The more intense and unrevealing the medical evaluations, the worse the patient got and the more the family became convinced that he was very ill with an undiagnosed medical illness.

What Mike's parents needed from me in that moment was for me to respect what they've been through. This sounds so obvious, but when emotions are running high and the family starts to question your competence with varying degrees of hostility, it can be hard not to get defensive, not to spout all the reasons you are right and—unspoken but loud and clear—they are wrong. One of the most valuable things that my colleagues taught me to do when I was at the receiving end of hostile, disrespectful pushback was to simply take a breath, remind myself that this is the illness talking, and focus on what will move us all forward, together. It took some practice, but over time it became easier to step back from the emotionality, recognize it as the symptom that it was, and keep the interaction as therapeutic as possible.

In addition to not casting doubt on what they all were experiencing from this illness, the family needed explanations that made space for the fact that they have a wonderful child who was not a liar, and was clearly suffering. They needed me to understand how afraid and frustrated they were, to not disregard their suffering or blame any of them, including Mike, for the situation. Sure, they may have been doctor shopping up and down the coast of California, but on the flip side, neurologist after neurologist—no doubt with best intentions—acquiesced to requests for more tests, more adaptive services, more medication trials, even as they brought up the likelihood that these events could be emotionally based. It was like one long, drawn out school note. One long, drawn out excused absence.

The family needed to hear our belief that these seizures were very real, even though they were not epilepsy or another neurologic condition. For their part they also needed to accept our plan to focus entirely on the emotional sources of this illness because we were convinced that was what would stop the convulsions.

These parents had been living in fear for quite some time, so I also needed to make clear to them that children with nonepileptic seizures rarely sustain any significant trauma. I also reminded them that Mike was in a children's hospital, on a unit that was co-managed by Pediatrics and Psychiatry. He would have pediatric eyes on him twenty-four hours a day. They needed to hear that if there were the slightest indication that Mike was not medically stable, that would be promptly addressed through the kinds of tests and consultations that were available to any other patient anywhere else in the hospital. Mike would be safe.

What do I avoid getting into at this first meeting? The diagnosis debate. The family agreed, 100 percent, long before they ever boarded that plane bound for Providence, that we would all accept the conclusions of the extensive diagnostic workups done in California and not pursue further medical workup here unless it was clearly indicated by some new development. We knew from experience that their commitment to that plan would fizzle down to about 50 percent by the time their plane landed at TF Green airport. We expected it to sink to a minus 1 percent by day three of the admission at which point both parents and patient would be convinced they have made a terrible mistake in coming to us.

We've asked a lot of this exhausted, stressed, jet-lagged, climate-challenged family over the course of that first in-person meeting. They had listened to Dr. Spencer, his psychiatrist, and Dr. Hagin, his psychologist, explain how the emotional brain was unconsciously driving Mike's seizures. In doing so, Dan and Sarah essentially asked that Mike and his parents do backflips with their brains. When they then listened to me, the "medical" person, reiterating and supporting the MedPsych treatment approach, their brows furrowed. They darted glances at one another. They were hoping for a little more focus on medical diagnoses and treatment from me. They asked me to comment, ironically, not on the nature of the seizures, but what I think about all this "emotional focus."

"*J'allez au* bathroom?"

This is the really tricky part. It's not like speaking to the family about type 2 diabetes. With that illness we have an intricate understanding of the complex physiological processes that have gone rogue, and that provides a clean logic to the treatments we recommend. But selling a parent on why the entire staff is going to ignore their child when he falls to the floor in a convulsion is a very different matter. That is awfully tricky to explain when we cannot precisely pinpoint the anatomy and physiology behind Mike's symptoms. We cannot fully trace the way the emotional brain signals Mike's arms and legs to flail the way we can explain the electrical discharges of epilepsy. A neuroscientist could currently explain just a fraction of the pathways involved in Mike's emotionally based illness, and most of us mortals would understand only about 10 percent of what he or she said about that small fraction.

We do at least know what we know. We do know that the emotional brain—itself a complex matrix that channels through many different areas of the brain—is driving this disorder. We know this as the mechanism of illness because treating the symptoms with a combination of functional and behavioral interventions make the child better. They make the seizures stop. That sure wouldn't work with epilepsy. In other words, the diagnosis will ultimately be validated by the fact that our treatment worked. For the parents and patient, our approach seems counterintuitive and requires a giant leap of faith from the point of admission to the point of discharge.

So how does the pediatrician respond when asked about "all this emotional focus?"

Carefully.

"We believe, based on lots of evidence, that Mike has a healthy brain. And yet he's still having these scary events. We are able to do something very unique here. We can apply our behavioral approaches in a place that is fully equipped to handle any medical issues. Your son is in a place where we know we can safely ignore his convulsions. He will have skilled medical eyes on him twenty-four hours a day. He may get a bump or a bruise but nothing more serious than he'd get on a soccer field. If there is any indication of something more serious happening, he will have an immediate medical assessment. If we observe anything even remotely concerning, we will not hesitate to get a neurologist or other specialist involved. Most importantly, experience shows us that this treatment approach will work for nonepileptic convulsions. I believe it will work for Mike."

Therein lies an important reality for all of us: the patient and family will typically remain more skeptical than hopeful until they start to see the results with their own eyes. The most important thing I can do for them in the moment is to convince them that Mike will, if nothing else, be safe.

Science and clinical experience were on my (and Mike's) side. The fact that his convulsions were occurring unconsciously did not mean they were occurring unrestrained. His motor cortex and cerebellum are still functioning perfectly well. What we see in nonepileptic seizures is that the non-emotional parts of the brain will still work to protect the patient. This means that we are likely to see Mike's body slump to the ground rather than face-plant or fall backwards, smashing the back of his head. That distinction often translates out in the nonmedical world as proof that the child is faking.

"If their convulsions are *real* why don't they get hurt? Why don't they lose bladder control? Why don't they turn blue?"

An understanding of MedPsych illness allows us to dispel that notion. Mike's emotional brain is firing on all cylinders to keep Mike at home, sheltered from the developmental expectations that for some reason are terrifying him. In order to accomplish this the emotional brain is controlling what the child or teen is *experiencing,* and Mike is absolutely experiencing convulsions. But the emotional brain is not overriding the rest of the brain. His EEG will be normal, his falls will be self-protective, and he is likely to maintain bowel and bladder control. Social inhibitions, emanating from the frontal cortex, are strong in teenagers.

Even as I became more therapeutically adept in my thinking and communication, nobody—family or staff—would have mistaken me for a psychiatrist or psychologist. This was not surprising or worrisome to myself or anyone else on the team. It wasn't my goal to talk like Dr. Spencer or think like Dr. Hagin. I had been thinking and talking like a pediatrician for decades and I would continue to do so. This nuanced distinction between team members illustrates the beauty of integrated care. We all bring different things to the table, even unconscious things like word choice and facial expressions. Like the pediatrician glancing at Mike every minute or so to make sure he looked okay as he slid off his chair and on to the conference room floor. If what Mike's family needed at that juncture was a little more pediatrics and a little less psych, I could supply that with full authenticity and still get the job done.

It is important to note that we made no clinical decisions without parent and patient input. In Mike's case the hardest part for them to accept was that we would observe but not react to or accommodate any seizure-like activity while Mike was on our unit. No hospital bed. No padding. If he slipped down to the floor during group therapy, the group would continue. If a convulsion was too distracting the group would move to another room. No one would soothe Mike, put a pillow under his head, or move a table out of his way. Removing "secondary gain"—all the attention and accommodation the patient gets for being ill—is the primary treatment for nonepileptic convulsions.

The nonepileptic seizure disorders that we treated on the unit seemed to me to have the quickest response to treatment of any other somatic symptom disorder or functional neurologic disorder illness I encountered. Theoretically it could be done as an outpatient. However, it is often asking too much of a parent to do this at home. It is nearly impossible to expect it to happen at school. It is a luxury to be able to carry it out so confidently on a medically staffed unit.

We all survived Mike's first family meeting, despite his dramatic convulsion towards the end. His parents, following our lead, managed to remain in their chairs and Sarah Hagin immediately started asking the parents more questions about what Mike was like as a child. I glanced one more time at Mike just long enough to see how good his color was, and then forced myself to look back at the group. This had been one long meeting.

Three weeks later, Mike was discharged to the MedPsych Partial (day) program. He had one seizure there his first day, and no recurrence. He also had a seizure at the Ronald McDonald House, where he and his folks were staying for the duration of the Partial admission. Mom, in an understandable lapse of confidence, called the Partial program director that Sunday morning and asked Dr. DerMarderosian if she should take Mike to the ER. Dr. D. talked her through our shared "benign neglect" approach again and Mom was able to manage it all on her own. As far as we know, that was the last seizure Mike ever had.

I realize that to a certain degree I was channeling Aristotle in that family meeting as much as I was the neuroscience. We know these illnesses are real. We have a general concept about cause and effect if not yet a fully constructed pathway. We know that certain behavioral interventions that have nothing to do with seizures or treatments of epilepsy will make the child better. We do what clearly works, even if we can't yet fully explain the brain physiology behind it.

Our twenty-first century version of vegetables and fresh air.

CHAPTER 6

Safe at Third

WHAT WAS MIKE, WITH HIS NONEPILEPTIC CONVUL-
sions, and his family already teaching us about the worried
Eleanors of the outpatient world? They bring the hallmark
features of all emotionally based illness, from common outpatient presentations to intense inpatient ones, into sharp focus. It is important
to reiterate that we don't really know *why* Eleanor didn't want to step
on that school bus waiting at the curb. And here's the fascinating thing
that Mike teaches us: we don't need to. Not usually. Not right away.
What we need to do is recognize that the primary symptom here is loss
of function, whether it is the severe impairment of educational, social,
and developmental function that Mike is experiencing, or the more
contained impact on school attendance that unfolded back in my outpatient office with little Eleanor.

Over the course of her office visit back then Eleanor's emotional illness was sending her Red Alerts that our conversation, way too focused
on feelings, was putting her in an unnamed danger. Abdominal pain was
her unconscious armor against whatever fears she could not name, and

the complex centers and pathways of her emotional brain were scream-ing at her to hold firm: *your stomach really, really hurts.* What patients like Mike brought into clear focus for me, even if it was in a rearview mirror, was that Eleanor's primary symptom was not abdominal pain. It was *functional loss*—school absenteeism. Functional loss is a cardinal feature of emotionally based illness.

As we saw in Eleanor's case her parents were picking up on her mounting anxiety that day in the office. They brought Eleanor to my office so I could help her, not for me to increase her distress, not to make the situation worse in their eyes. They were starting to worry that this nice doctor wasn't taking their concerns seriously. With all that, it was no surprise that the conversation kept circling back to Mom's request for a pediatric gastroenterology evaluation. This is *treatment resistance*—another confounding, frustrating, and expected symptom of emo-tionally based illness. It is a much milder form than what Mike and his family demonstrated on their two-year journey through the world of medical specialists back in California. But it was there, in my office that day, loud and clear. MedPsych teaches us that the best antidotes for treatment resistance are trust between providers and the family, mini-mal attention to what the medical diagnoses may or may not be, and a focus on restoring function.

It's common to interpret family resistance incorrectly. What I would see as Eleanor's parents' inability to recognize this as school anxiety and their insistence, against all evidence, that there just had to be a medical cause, would often stir up a reaction of dismay in me. It seemed that the parents were inexplicably oblivious to the clear evidence in front of them. It seemed they were not being strong enough.

But now I know the humbling truth. I was not being smart enough.

Eleanor and her family did not come to my office that morning for a fresh take on her absenteeism. They came because she needed per-mission to not go to school. They all knew that that would make her feel better, even if none of them knew why. And her parents certainly didn't come in to watch their daughter's distress escalate. They wanted their little girl to feel better. The approach I was recommending, however—getting back to school—triggered immediate distress in Eleanor. A focus on emotions rather than lab tests or referrals is challenging the family in ways that I found frustrating. But treatment resistance and family enmeshment, when understood as symptoms of this illness, are also our guideposts to treatment. My experience on MedPsych taught me that it's not fair or accurate to view the parents in this situation as simply not rising to the occasion.

When it came time to talk to Eleanor directly, I knew not to challenge her as to whether she "really" had pain. Instead, I told her that I believed "worry" was causing it. This was a pretty standard pediatric approach and is aligned somewhat with MedPsych treatment in that it acknowledges the need to reconnect the child with her feelings.

But back in those outpatient days this wording was more a show of kindness and discretion than an enlightened view. I did not fully grasp how real her experience of pain actually was, and how unaware she was of her anxieties about school. Back in those days I could hit a triple out to right field, reassuring Eleanor that her body was working very well, explaining that worry was the root of the problem, and that what would help the most was to practice talking about feelings because that makes them less scary. I would then move on to the plan: a stepwise approach to getting out the door in the morning, getting her into the school building even when she is reporting pain, and recruiting the help of teachers and the school nurse in the process. This was often successful.

What I couldn't do was hit a home run. I couldn't look her in the eye and say, "I *know* your pain is real. I know you are not faking."

I couldn't say that because I didn't know that. I assumed that Eleanor, a sweet kid, had been forced into using lies and manipulation out of sheer desperation. She saw no other recourse. I also could not explain to her that her emotional brain was actually tricking her body, signaling it to feel real symptoms, because I had little understanding of that myself. And I struggled not to grow defensive by the parents' resistance to my recommendations. I had not yet learned that treatment resistance was a cardinal feature of this disorder. They were doing their best to protect their child. I did not understand the extent to which the whole family and even the wider community got caught up in this.

Eleanor and her parents were trapped in a worry cycle that was hard to break. Getting Eleanor back into school was going to cause all of them distress, and most of us avoid distress whenever possible. We especially want to avoid seeing our children in distress. When I explained to Eleanor and her folks that the best treatment for this situation was to get Eleanor back to school in a planful, supportive way, I could accept Eleanor's resistance. But I was thrown off by the sudden change in Mom's tone as she requested a gastroenterology evaluation.

"I just think you've done everything you can here, Doctor. We need another opinion. There is clearly something medical going on here."

There would come a time when I would see all this distress and resistance that was coming to the surface as progress. But not back then. Not as I watched Eleanor clinging to her father, sobbing into the jacket of his business suit as her mother quickly gathered their things. Suddenly alone in the exam room I would think to myself, "Why is this so hard?"

It was a rhetorical question. I never dreamed I'd one day learn the answer.

During those many years of outpatient practice there was frequently an eye-rolling Greek chorus in the background of these kinds of encounters:

The Teacher, (impatiently) referring to helicopter parents and lamenting to me on the phone that she can't believe how manipulative the child was.

"I mean, she seems so sweet, but she has those parents wrapped around her little fingers."

The Nurse, (knowingly) reminiscing about how she handled her own kids.

"They knew they had to be bleeding before I'd let them stay home."

The Coach, (kindheartedly) bending the rules about coming to practice if the child hadn't attended class that day.

"She's such a good kid."

The Pediatrician, (ironically) marveling at how such smart parents struggled to see what was actually going on...

My experience with emotionally based illness on the MedPsych unit taught me things that were immensely helpful for patients like Eleanor. But it also revealed the uncomfortable truth that I had often been treating kiddos like Eleanor with one hand tied behind my back. It took a deep dive into the world of MedPsych illness to raise this pediatrician's knowledge to where it would meet the science.

Yes, I understood early on that an anxiety-based illness cannot get better without restoring the child's ability to do whatever it was they were avoiding. Hence the behavioral plan for gradually getting back in school, backed up with some coping skills or therapy if needed. And although my instincts told me it would not be helpful to imply that a child was faking or lying, avoidance of these terms was more an exercise in good manners than a legitimate medical assessment.

What do I wish I knew back then? Pain is pain. What working with MedPsych patients taught me was that the physical pain and suffering that these children are experiencing are very real—whether it's showing up in their healthy abdomen or their post-concussed head or their anatomically perfect left knee. We need to understand that this is not consciously deceptive behavior. It is happening because the patients are disconnected from their actual underlying emotions and are experiencing this decoy symptom instead. It is important to point out here that people do fake illnesses, but that is very different, as we will see further on.

I also wish I had a better appreciation of the fact that parents get pulled into the illness not because they are clueless but because that's what the illness does. They are trying to avoid distress in their child. It is what all parents are wired to do, and can be very difficult to override. Every pulse of protective instinct in their bodies is telling Eleanor's parents that first and foremost they needed to alleviate Eleanor's distress.

Last but not least, Eleanor's illness underscores the role of *accommodation* in these disorders. When I wrote that vague school note that the principal was requiring, confirming that Eleanor was seen in my office that day for abdominal pain (that was the only information the parents would consent to) I was accommodating the illness as well. I told myself it bought me more time and breathing room to work with this family. It lowered everyone's distress level. I came to understand, even before my MedPsych days, that we do more harm than good when we excuse absences. Absent is absent. It requires no assignment of validity. And absence in this setting is as detrimental to the child as it is to the kid who simply can't get out of bed on time. Perhaps more so. The underlying causes of absence need to be identified and addressed with compassion. Not excused.

I know firsthand now that when medical providers fully understand the nature of emotionally driven illness it changes our mindsets and our reactions. It bestows appropriate legitimacy on the child's experience. It sharpens our clinical skills and adds authenticity to our compassion. It aligns us with the family and evokes trust in the therapeutic process.

It gets us more home runs.

CHAPTER 7

Curves and Climbs

I HAD SO MUCH TO LEARN AS THE FIRST MEDICAL DIRECTOR of the MedPsych unit. In fact, it would be my task to fully define the role. If I had been more aware of how steep the learning curve would be for me to do the job, I might have concluded I was not the right person for it. On the other hand, the MedPsych and Adolescent Med staff that interviewed me seemed to collectively shrug at steep learning curves. It made more sense in retrospect. This was a groundbreaking program. The innovative folks who created it were looking for a well-rounded pediatrician who knew what she knew and didn't know and who was open to learning new things. I'd say those are strong suits for most pediatricians. Just as importantly, the doctors interviewing me were specialists working in a teaching hospital, tasked with training the next generation of doctors. They were by design willing, confident teachers.

In one of my early interviews I was fascinated to learn that my future co-director of the unit, Dan Spencer, was "double-boarded." He was certified in both pediatrics and child psych. Dan was decades younger than me, but had already acquired the calm, kind, reassuring manner it takes most of us years to develop. In one of my early interviews Dan was telling me about a few of the recent admissions to the unit. He mentioned functional neurologic disorder or FND—previously known as conversion disorder—and somatic symptom disorder as the two most common disorders that were referred to us.

Dan did not blink when I asked him to "remind" me what the difference was between a somatic symptom disorder and FND He proceeded to explain FND to me in the same simple, respectful way I would hear him explain it to our families over the coming years. FND was the presentation of emotional illness as a neurologic symptom rather than a "somatic" (bodily) symptom like pain. So a teen with an emotionally driven illness whose legs are paralyzed, or who feels numbness in their arms, without any evidence of a physical malfunction in his nervous system, has a functional neurologic disorder because these symptoms mimic a neurologic problem. Mike's nonepileptic convulsions fit into this category, as his symptoms mimicked epilepsy, a neurologic condition. Aches and pains on the other hand—unexplained abdominal pain or headaches that keep a kiddo from attending school, or mysterious joint pain that lands the child in a wheelchair because it's too painful to stand up—represent somatic symptom disorder. Eleanor, with her belly pain, had a relatively mild version of somatic symptom disorder. As Dan so patiently explained to me during that early interview, both of these disorders come under the heading of MedPsych illness—emotional distress being unconsciously deflected into physical symptoms.

I would learn that from a MedPsych point of view, the treatments of FND and somatic symptom disorders are pretty much the same: rehabilitate the loss of physical function—the inability to walk for example—whether it was due to weakness (FND) or pain (somatic symptom disorder), in a therapeutic environment that allows the patient to fully experience their own emotions as their function improves. But on that interview day I was still months away from being able to have that sentence roll off my tongue like I truly owned it.

It was this conversation that was resurfacing months later as we talked about an upcoming admission of a child who couldn't feel their legs. I winced at the memory.

"Didn't that interview worry you a little, Dan? I mean, it must have felt like you were hiring a pastry chef to work in a sushi bar."

"No," he laughed. "I knew you were going to be great. We are so lucky to have you."

There it was, right from the beginning. That generous optimism. I'll allow myself credit for giving off a vibe that I was always eager to learn. Dan, like all the other MedPsych providers who interviewed me, took that vibe and ran with it. He focused on my strengths, patiently filled in the psychiatric gaps in my experience, and redirected my misconceptions. I would learn firsthand over the coming years that how the MedPsych staff developed as professionals and how our sick patients found their paths to recovery mirrored each other in remarkable ways. We all got frustrated. We learned patience. We all came to understand the mechanism of this devouring disorder. We all, patients and caregivers, were transformed in ways large and small by our clinical successes.

But that supportive optimism is the glossy finish. The day-to-day struggles were often fuzzier and painful.

I remember an episode in rounds from when I was fairly new on the unit. A nurse that was filling in from another unit was expressing her frustration with one of the patients, Jenny, who refused to cooperate with vital signs.

"If you ask me, she was just being a brat."

This prompted a new mental health worker to chime in.

"That's how she was with me all day yesterday. Very manipulative. I guess she's always been allowed to get away with that rude kind of behavior at home."

My newbie mental reaction to all this was something along the lines of a vague *Huh. This doesn't sound okay.*

And then Dan, who had been leading rounds, jumped in. His tone was calm and reasonable, but I detected a note of frustration that I hadn't heard before from him in rounds.

"This girl was horribly traumatized in the past," he said, speaking slowly. "She is terrified. She feels powerless. This is why she is behaving like she is. We need to remain compassionate and professional, even though that can be very hard to do when she is being difficult. It is why we are all here. We all know how hard this work is and we are only human. When we are getting frustrated then we pause or we step away, and seek out another team member for support. We Don't. Blame. The Patient."

Dan's quiet but passionate redirection that morning in rounds left a lasting impression on me. It was already obvious to me that I had to be constantly checking myself against this standard. It got even trickier when I needed to intervene with other staff. But as Dan reminded us all that morning, the expectation was that if another staff member offered to relieve you in an interaction you were having with a patient, you agreed. Immediately. If you had questions, you asked them of the other team member later.

It wasn't long after that day in rounds when I was heading back to my office to wrap up the evening. Most of the providers had already gone home. As was often the case this time of night it was just me and the nurses and the mental health workers. As I opened the door to my office I heard a mental health worker speaking very sharply to a patient regarding what the MHW referred to as her "bad attitude." It was the tone that first raised my antennae, but it was the continuation of the harangue that alarmed me. The staff person just kept going on and on, overtalking the patient, towering over the girl as she sat in her chair looking up at the MHW. I turned around and surveyed the area. The charge nurse was off to the side talking to another patient, but glancing intermittently at the upsetting scene a few feet away. I steeled myself for the task I would have loved to avoid.

"Hey Sue, why don't you take a break. I can take over."

Sue was not pleased and gave me pushback. Meanwhile the nurse, who was the MHW's immediate supervisor, still hung back as if it didn't involve her. I insisted that I take over for Sue in what was an increasingly awkward exchange in the presence of a patient, and the MHW stormed off while I then attempted to do damage control with the wide-eyed group of patients that had been within earshot. The MHW filed a complaint with the head nurse the next day regarding my disrespectful behavior toward her and took it to Human Resources as well.

There were so many things wrong with that scenario. The MHW's behavior toward the patient. The inaction of her supervisor. The MHW's refusal to step back when I intervened. And the pounding headache I drove home with that night. There was no question in my mind that I needed to intervene when I did. But the team drama that ensued over the next few days in response to my handling of the incident underscored the adage that no good deed ever goes unpunished. I gritted my teeth at the knowledge that Dan would have been much less likely to endure all the second-guessing and defensiveness that followed my decisions. Dan was a strong leader who led by example. But at the end of the day, I felt like I had to be the braver one.

I would often think back to these kinds of incidents during my tenure on the unit—as staff came and went, as an occasional consultant would make a snide remark, as I myself felt a wave of frustration wash over me at a disrespectful teen. And I thought about it when I eventually took over the job of running morning rounds. It never got easy to call a colleague out regarding their attitude toward their patient, or to remain steady in the face of disrespect, or to deal with the consequences of ruffled feathers, but it got slightly less hard.

Troublesome employees were a small minority on our unit but, as in other healthcare settings, they can have an outsized negative impact on morale and staffing because there are often no effective systems in place to deal with such problems. Employees who become toxic to the workplace tend as a group to use up more compensated sick time, in turn placing more burden on their colleagues who have to pick up the slack. They may also have an inflated sense of self-importance and blame others for their mistakes, especially when stress levels rise. Demoralizing, distracting drama ensues.

Healthcare institutions need to heal themselves so that their self-protective mindsets are not at odds with maintaining a healthy workplace. Employees really do need Human Resources because egregious things really do happen. We all are painfully aware of that. I lived through it myself in my early medical career. But Human Resources is not always the best place to deal with toxic employees. An employee who is excessively absent, takes no responsibility for their own performance, and actually believes the problems they cause are always someone else's fault, can evoke the same sympathy from an unwitting HR representative as an employee who has suffered harmful discrimination.

Just as my experience on MedPsych shone an unflinching light on my previous outpatient management of emotionally based illness, the staff dynamics on the unit, with its share of conflict and drama, reminded me of the smaller-scale drama of running a primary care practice, and those same kinds of interpersonal distractions that sapped our energies. Again I found myself thinking "If I only knew then what I know now."

What do I see more clearly now? These workplace issues would be better addressed in the realm of occupational medicine rather than Human Resources, and new doctors in training need to be offered some basic skills to manage these inevitable scenarios, for their own protection and for that of their hardworking employees. My MedPsych experience underscored for me that healthcare institutions need occupational medicine physicians who understand the dynamics of these situations, and can spot them. Occupational medicine physicians need to be trained in how to reconcile challenging employee behavior with appropriate management styles and work environments. They need to provide guidance and support not only to the underperforming employee who persistently feels he or she has been treated poorly, but also to the people they blame for their poor performances, and to their supervisors who may need to learn modified management techniques.

This is what the struggling employee needs, especially when said employee has chosen highly stressful work. This is also what his or her colleagues need so they can continue to do their jobs undistracted by the drama. The MedPsych universe convinced me that this is what health-care entities need if they are going to care for all their staff—the under-performing ones and the ones trying to hold everything together—with the same dedication that they show for patients. The two, after all, are inseparable.

CHAPTER 8

There is No Try

ALYSSA WAS A FOURTEEN-YEAR-OLD GIRL WITH DEBILI-tating abdominal pain and weight loss who was referred to us from a prestigious medical center in Boston. Her symptoms came under the category of somatic symptom disorder as they were "bodily" or "somatic" complaints as opposed to a neurologic symptom such as Mike's convulsions.

Alyssa had been fed by a tube through her stomach for months because attempting to eat food caused too much abdominal pain. Doctor after doctor found no definitive pathology in her gastrointestinal tract. Test after invasive test turned up normal or negative. Alyssa had gradually shifted to a gluten-free vegan diet and she and her parents all hoped she could remain on that diet in our program despite the fact that her symptoms continued to grow worse even with that restriction. One of the expectations we needed to agree on in our preadmission communications was that we would be moving Alyssa towards what her normal diet had been *before* her illness. In her case, that had been a pretty typical teen diet.

Our plan was also to gradually move her to taking all her food by mouth. Food choices would be made by the parents, with the support of a dietician. We did this for several reasons. Her parents would be the most reliable source of Alyssa's prior eating history. This also gave the parents back power that the illness had taken from them: the power to ensure that Alyssa was getting what her body needed rather than allowing their decisions to be influenced by her emotional distress. At the same time, we would gradually introduce oral feedings while we decreased tube feedings. We would carry this out with close medical monitoring and consultation with the Eating Disorder team.

Alyssa and her parents expressed their skepticism that this would work, but agreed to "give it a try." I learned that "trying" was a common hiding place for treatment resistance and accommodation: "I'm really trying. It's just not working. It's not my fault I can't do what you ask."

Dan was fond of quoting Yoda at this point.

"Do, or do not. There is no Try."

I would laugh about what a nerdy thing that was to say, but I had to admit, Yoda seemed very tuned in to the MedPsych mindset.

Families often assume we will not continue with our preadmission plan once we see how sick their child actually is. We expected the first few weeks would be tough. Tough for them. Tough for us. It felt especially tough for the pediatrician in the days following admission since families almost always start out very "medically" focused, and the pediatricians—myself or my new partner, Linda Doberstein—were the only ones in the room for whom the medical issues were front and center. Parents were often surprised and disappointed to hear that we continued to fully support the proposed therapeutic plan even after meeting their child and seeing how impaired she was. They would question our clinical abilities.

Not wanting to start off too harsh, one or the other parent would say something along the lines of, "Doctor, we're sure you are very good at what you do, but you have to understand that our daughter has been seen by many specialists who were experts in their field. They were all convinced that this was a medical condition. We don't fault you. We just feel you probably haven't seen anything like this before."

They knew I had reviewed all the medical records and had spoken to several of the specialists they had seen. They knew the specialists found no medical explanation for Alyssa's symptoms. Why would they lie about what the specialists had said? I wouldn't exactly call it lying.

The first errors of thought were simple. Alyssa's parents were doing what parents instinctively want to do when their child is distressed: run interference. Their perspective had been distorted by Alyssa's scary illness and they were stuck in a reverse logic of sorts. Her parents were focusing on all the doctor visits, all the tests, and all the days and weeks and months that this illness had been at the center of their lives. How could there be nothing wrong medically with their daughter when their entire lives had been taken over by her medical needs?

That brings us to the second distortion—one that sits squarely on the specialists' shoulders. The parents' distorted beliefs were unintentionally upheld by the hesitancy doctors often feel about telling their patients they don't entirely "believe" them. The same doctors who reassured me on the phone that they found no evidence of medical pathology, and who were so relieved she was headed to our program, had been much more "diplomatic" when speaking to the family.

Emotionally based illness loves diplomacy. It's like a faded crosswalk on a shady road, where what is really needed is a high speed bump. Alyssa's illness kept getting pushed down that road until she finally got to us, the big bump. So were the parents lying when they insisted the previous specialists had been very concerned about Alyssa's medical symptoms? Not exactly. The specialists *had* been concerned but expressed that concern with too much diplomacy. And hitting a speed bump at full speed is jarring. It can make your head spin.

Alyssa's parents urged me to call their most recent outpatient specialist so he could explain the nature of Alyssa's illness to me. I told them in as gentle a way as I could that I had already spoken to two of the most recent specialists and they both wholeheartedly agreed with our course of treatment. The parents looked surprised and offended. And still quite skeptical.

At this point in the family meeting, while my heart rate was getting a bit on the high side, Dan and Sarah seemed to be calmly letting everything play out. I took some comfort in the fact that they were not interjecting. I knew them well enough by now to not mistake this for politeness. If they were still sitting back in their chairs it was because they thought I was holding my own.

The first few weeks were an uphill slog in the face of Alyssa's fear and anger, the parents' skepticism, and the team's own human reactions to all the drama. It was not unusual to hear frustration from the mental health worker who watched Alyssa pour her cereal on the floor, and then insist it was an accident, or to hear exasperation in the nurse who could not get her to cooperate with vital signs for the third day in a row. Frustration was in my voice as well, in those early days, when I reported in rounds that I still had not completed a full physical exam, able only to listen to the heart one day, do a neurologic exam the next. It was really important to me that I do a thorough job, and I was being thwarted.

The parents were tough too. I frequently found myself on the receiving end of their disrespect. They would scoff at my assessments and demand second opinions. But as was typical for many of our patients, Alyssa's parents had run out of options and had nowhere else to turn. Each emotional threat to leave was followed by a reluctant agreement to stay—at least until they could come up with a better plan. At that early point in my MedPsych tenure I was exhausted by the onslaught of anger and disrespect. I was also worried. I noted Alyssa's slowed heart rate due to malnutrition, and worried about what her self-imposed starvation was doing to her brain. I worried about her lack of mobility and muscle wasting. I worried that if she left, she might eventually die of this illness.

Mining for Gold

I SLOWLY LEARNED AND CAME TO ACCEPT THAT A NEW FAMILY would, in an emotional tailspin, often spend the first two to three weeks of admission resisting the agreed upon plan, arguing for medical evaluation and even insulting us and openly undermining our therapeutic recommendations. I came to view it as an emotional fever. It doesn't feel good, much the same way an actual fever can make a child irritable and achy. But it is a very good sign that the infection has been properly identified by the body and the child's immune system is kicking in. The physical distress caused by a high body temperature is unpleasant but underlies the path to recovery. The distress caused by shining daylight on suppressed emotions—also unpleasant—serves much the same purpose.

While I expressed my frustration and worry about all the pushback from Alyssa's family, Dan and Sarah accepted it with a realism I had not yet cultivated.

"It's not up to us," Dan would shrug. "Alyssa is very sick, but she is in no imminent danger. They will stay or they will leave. We hope they'll stay. We know how to help them, but only if they are ready for help. If they do leave, we'll make sure they have a plan in place, and maybe we'll have at least planted that seed that will help them accept MedPsych treatment in the future."

With the help of a small army of psychologists and psychiatrists, I did come to understand and accept this tenacious form of treatment resistance. To let go of a medical focus on their child's illness implied to many parents that their child was lying. They know their child and do not believe this. It also can sound like "it's all in his head," which sounds dismissive rather than helpful. And it triggers tremendous guilt. What parent among us would not ask ourselves where we went wrong?

Patients and families are often also coping with a slow wave of grief over the months or years that have been lost from their lives, and the toll the illness has taken on their family life and finances. To access and embrace everybody's underlying emotions this admission will feel as dangerous to Alyssa and her family as a powder keg at a barbecue.

So of course we have to expect distress and resistance in our patients. This is why the dietician is not surprised when she hears from Alyssa on week two:

"Dr. Kozel said I could eat my lunch in my room today."

The experienced dietician doesn't believe it. She knows that social eating will be a big part of Alyssa's recovery, and she also knows that if any detail in the behavior plan had been changed, she would have heard it directly from me first. But like a kiddo with the flu, Alyssa's emotional fever is in high gear. She and the family are trying to undermine the treatment plan. At times, and out of desperation, they will even intentionally mislead us and try to split the providers against each other. And they will decide to leave many times over.

Alyssa, for instance, would report to me, "Dr. Hagin said I didn't have to go to group therapy today because my stomach is really hurting."

Dr. Hagin would take this completely in stride during rounds.

"So of course I didn't say that. We talked about things she could do to manage her pain and anxiety but the expectation for attending group therapy has not changed."

Patients and families soon came to realize that all the different members of the team communicated every day about each patient. "Splitting," as Alyssa's behavior is called, is a form of treatment resistance. The patient will try to sow confusion about what the plan actually is. These attempts to split the providers are just more emotional fever. And it can be helpful to her team. As we see what triggers the distress (Alyssa's meal expectation had been increased the day before) it points us to what purpose this illness is serving for the patient, whether it be keeping the parents together, avoiding the social and emotional expectations of adolescence, anxiety about one's sexuality, a restrictive eating disorder ... the list goes on. The psychological purpose the illness serves for the patient varies, but there is always a purpose. Identifying that unconscious purpose opens up the road to recovery.

Dr. Spencer may have been able to channel Yoda for guidance. I found my own Jedi master.

Dr. Fran Pingatore is an advanced practice nurse who specializes in psychotherapy. She wore many hats around the hospital, including being a consultant to the MedPsych staff. Fran sat in on our rounds and many of our meetings and I quickly learned the value of paying close attention to what she noticed and what she said.

In one of my early department head meetings, Fran picked up on what the nurse manager was saying about the attitudes of some of the staff towards a problematic patient. Fran commented on the worrisome "countertransference" that she witnessed in rounds, and advised us to provide some education on transference and countertransference at our next staff in-service meeting. From the nods and comments that followed, it looked like everyone else in the room knew exactly what she was referring to and agreed it was concerning.

Transference? Countertransference? I probably hadn't heard those terms since I was in med school, and yet here they were, many decades later, alive and well on the top floor of Hasbro Children's Hospital.

I looked at Fran's open face. Anybody could ask her anything. And I did:

"So, remind me—what are we calling transference and countertransference in this situation?"

Fran did the minutest of double takes and then said something general about the unconscious interactions between patients and providers.

"Does that make sense?" she asked.

"Um I guess. I still can't tell which is transference and which is countertransference," I answered honestly, reminded once again of just how different I was from every other person in the room.

But the driving force of this program, which Fran had been instrumental in developing, was the conviction that pediatric and psychiatric care could be truly integrated in a meaningful way. Fran was a confident, generous teacher, and she was on a mission.

"No problem," she responded with an encouraging smile. "Why don't we grab a few minutes together after this meeting and we can talk some more?"

A short while later we found a quiet spot in the empty hallway outside the unit.

"So have any of the patients gotten on your nerves lately?"

"Sure," I replied. That was an easy one. "Alyssa."

"Okay, what happened with Alyssa this morning?"

"Well," I said, "she was refusing her bloodwork, and I was trying to explain why the nutritionists requested it, and what that would tell us."

"Uh huh. And what happened?"

"She was being very disrespectful, dropping f-bombs every other word, telling me that I didn't know what I was doing, that she wanted a new doctor. Just really giving me a hard time. I got pretty frustrated."

"Uh huh," she said again. "And why do you think she was behaving like that?"

"Well..." I said, realizing that in my frustration I hadn't focused as much attention on the *why* as I was on the *whining.* "I'm assuming because she's terrified about being here, and furious with her parents for allowing it. I'm sure the idea of taking more blood out of her was not helping either."

The arrival of *why* in my head may have been delayed, but it seemed pretty obvious when I said it out loud. Pediatrics 101.

There was that giant grin again. "Exactly," Fran said. "And you reacted in a very understandable way. You got annoyed with her. This is pure gold. So why does all this matter?"

"I dunno," I said with a shrug. "It means I need to be a little more patient?"

"Well I'm thinking that this might be the reaction she evokes from a lot of the other staff too. And probably from her family. We don't know that yet, but being aware of the reaction she evoked in you can give you important insight into the dynamics of this child's illness. It's all good!" she reiterated.

"Okay," I said with a sigh. "So we know she's mad at her parents for keeping her here, and she's lumping me in with them as one of the adults making her life miserable. And I reacted to her the way a lot of people in her life have been reacting to her—with frustration."

"Yes!" smiled Fran.

"Rather than seeing it as a symptom," I added

"Yes! You've got it!" she answered triumphantly.

"So what part is transference and what part is countertransference?" I asked.

Triumph took a breath.

"So Alyssa's behavior was transference. She was directing all her emotional mess at you. The way you reacted to it was countertransference. You were trying to help her and she basically rejected that. You are a person who wants to help people, and you know how to help her, but she wasn't letting you. She was being irrational. That stirred up an emotional reaction in you—frustration, or whatever you want to call it—and that my friend is countertransference.

"This stuff is pure gold," Fran continued. "We're going to talk a whole lot more about this."

And we did. Over the coming years we talked a great deal about psychoanalytic topics. I was in awe of her. How could she hear the exact same conversation I did and come away with twice as much useful information? Fran in turn never seemed to get frustrated with my thought processes, never made me feel like an outsider.

My interactions with Alyssa started to make so much sense. Pediatricians are very much in touch with the "whys" in a patient's or family's problematic behavior. However, whether by nature or nurture, we tend as a group to want to relieve distress, not embrace it. I was working hard to engage Alyssa in her own care, to connect with her as the intelligent young woman that she was. And she was having none of it. Her distress expanded to fill the room. I in turn saw that distress as a bad thing, as something that put me on the defensive, something I needed to quell.

I think it's fair to say that most pediatricians most of the time do not aim to push their families into emotional distress. My own personality was well suited to calming down a child, reassuring a parent, having everyone leave the office feeling better than when they walked in. And to be fair to us as a group, most families aren't expecting their pediatricians to move them to distress either, and are likely to think we're just being jerks when we do. It's hard to pull off this kind of therapeutic interaction in an outpatient pediatric setting. But it's safe to say that even in outpatient treatment, where the emotional illness is much less intense, the child is not going to move past an emotional roadblock without experiencing distress. The grownups in her life—parents, pediatrician, teacher—need to be able to tolerate that, and see it as an opportunity for progress.

Understanding transference and countertransference taught me a practical skill in a basic way that served me well. I learned to stop and name the emotions in the room—mine as well as everyone else's. No matter the distress level in the air, that simple skill instantly transformed me from participant in the illness to being one of the healers. It also saved me a lot of headaches.

Pure gold indeed. The longer I was part of the MedPsych team, and the wider my circle of teachers and supporters grew, the more I shared in their confidence and hopefulness. I was very aware of the irony: thanks to a remarkable bunch of psychiatry and psychology professionals I was still becoming, late in my career, the best pediatrician I had ever been.

CHAPTER 10

Motivating Dialogue

MEDPSYCH TREATMENT FOR ADOLESCENTS CENTERS around the patient's willingness to recover. Unlike much of conventional medicine, the patient cannot be passive. You cannot just swallow a pill or get an IV or have a surgeon yank out your swollen appendix in order to recover. By definition MedPsych treatment requires the patient to not just participate but actually drive the treatment process. Motivation is the medicine.

Any parent who has had to drag a reluctant sixteen-year-old out of bed in the morning and get her to school knows what a challenge this can be. What we are asking our patients to do is so much bigger. We are asking them to grapple with deeply entrenched fears on a daily basis and make difficult choices every step of the way so they can get their life back. We give them a lot of support, from the mental health worker who checks in with the patients every morning and evening in community meeting, to the nurse that coaches them to use their coping skills at 2:00 a.m., to the psychologist who helps them untangle their emotions in the privacy of a quiet office several times a week. The therapies they receive—the rehabilitative and nutritional ones, the pain management, the behavioral and the medical—all provide an integrated system of scaffolding to make success possible. But the central piece is always the patient's motivation.

This was a concept that came around full circle for me when I began working on the MedPsych unit. It was often frustrating when I couldn't convince a teenager why they should change a behavior. Imploring, bribing, and punishment were useless. Frustration was the enemy.

"Alyssa, you say you're doing fine, but here you are in this hospital you don't want to be in. We can help, if you'll let us." I may have been congratulating myself on my reasonable choice of words even as I spoke them.

"Get the f#*% out of here!" she screamed in response, pulling her blanket over her head and facing the wall.

I had once again underestimated how quickly a teen can go from somnolent to shrieking.

Shortly after that deflating meeting with the back of Alyssa's head, I was in morning rounds and heard for the second time that day how Alyssa refused to get up for her morning meds and vital signs. The psychologist spoke up out of turn and asked simply, "What does she want?"

I looked up at Dr. Hagin, perplexed by her odd question. The mental health worker, however, understood Dr. Hagin's question perfectly.

"She's complaining about not being allowed to listen to music," he responded with a shrug. "She might respond to that."

I felt a mental twitch at the notion of what sounded to me like bribery. This was not a toddler we were talking about. It was a sixteen-year-old girl.

Pediatricians know a thing or two about positive reinforcement. We need to. Young children are not the most rational creatures on earth. We spend a lot of time counseling parents on the limited ability of a preschooler to respond to logic when they are exhibiting undesirable behaviors. We look at exhausted parents, mere shadows of who they used to be, straight in the eye and talk about the power of incentives (rewards for good behavior) rather than disincentives (punishment). We encourage them to "catch their children being good" more than they admonish them for misbehaving. When it comes to behavioral modification, rewards are often the strongest currency we hold. Adolescents certainly respond to positive reinforcement as well, but a lot of the time we fall back on rationality when talking with adolescents. It is easy to forget we all have an inner toddler—especially when we're frightened.

"Okay," said Dr. Hagin to the team. "I'll talk to her after rounds."

When rounds ended I asked Sarah if I could join her.

"That actually would be great," she nodded. "You can support how important it is for her to take her meds."

I thought I was signing up to be in the audience, but Dr. Hagin was putting me to work. We found Alyssa lounging in her bed and as we approached, she rolled over to face the window.

"Alyssa, we need to talk," said Dr. Hagin. "Can you look at me?"

Alyssa rolled over and resurrected the earlier tirade. She worked her way through why she shouldn't have to get up so early, how much she hated this place, how she didn't even need those meds anymore and how stupid we all were. There were many possible counterpoints. I knew that because I was ticking them off in my head as she spoke. But Sarah sailed past them, as if they had nothing to do with why we were all gathered in the room.

"Dr. Kozel, is there a reason Alyssa needs to take her meds at the same time every day?"

I was starting to catch Sarah's drift. We were not going to do battle with Alyssa's stubbornness. We were going to invite her into a conversation about how best she could take care of herself, give her some sense of power. Without having made a conscious decision on how to answer, I found my responses mimicking the reasonable tone of Sarah's voice. I veered away from counterpoints and simply offered information I hoped she would find helpful.

"This medicine helps boost the chemicals in your brain that we all rely on to feel like ourselves. But the med only works well if you keep a constant level of it in your brain. Otherwise, you start to get withdrawal symptoms and that feels terrible. It means lots of side effects with little benefit."

Alyssa interrupted me a few times, mostly with snorts and groans, but there were those other times when her eyes told me was listening.

Sarah jumped in, taking the helm back from the less experienced pediatrician. "I know you want to feel better and go home Alyssa, but we need to know you can take care of yourself and keep yourself safe. How can we help you do that?"

How can we help you do that? I loved the question, even before I was able to unpack it. I heard how different it sounded from my own declarative "We want to help you," which in retrospect sounded not only like she was the passive recipient of our "help" but also a little like we were the ones who needed something, not her. We needed her to behave in order to do our jobs.

I started watching Sarah more than Alyssa, mesmerized by the way she could navigate these rocky waters, tying in Alyssa's stated goal—a jailbreak—with what we all wanted for her: to lead a healthy, fulfilling life.

"I don't know," Alyssa pouted, kicking her foot at the blankets, like a small frustrated child.

"The staff tells me you like music. What if we could arrange to have you listen to music for a little while after you take your meds? We know it's hard right now for you to get up out of bed and over to the nurse's station. Maybe the music would give you something nice to look forward to. Staff would have to sit with you, for safety, but I know they would be willing to do that."

No judgment. No expecting her to have the same motivations we did. Working very hard to frame our perspective that we are a team that Alyssa was part of and that the staff listened to her and cared about her. Sarah was explaining to her why the behavior we asked for was important, and then helping her to be able to make that decision herself with the promise of a meaningful reward.

It worked. Not perfectly but pretty well. Well enough that Alyssa started showing up for her meds. Gradually her ten minutes of music expanded to twenty minutes if she participated in community meeting, and then thirty minutes if she cooperated with vital signs and lab tests. In a surprisingly short time she accepted most of the expectations of the unit—not because she had no choice, but because her experience of them ranged from mildly annoying to useful to even pleasant as she made friends and mastered Uno. Once she was actively participating in group meeting Sarah was taking her off unit so she could use her own personal electronics. Alyssa would still let us know when she got mad. That's for sure. But mostly she began to see the path that would get her out of the hospital and back to her life. Her previous life. She saw that we cared about who she was, not what the illness had made her. It was amazing to me that so much of this grew from a tiny seed of nuanced communication.

Many young pediatricians today get training in the concept of motivational interviewing: a way to communicate with patients that respects their own perspectives and agency. The focus is on connecting with the patient and their own goals, acknowledging how hard change is, and supporting their abilities to bring about the change they desire. To be honest, when I first started hearing about this concept as an outpatient pediatrician I thought it sounded nice. Nice in the way pediatricians like to be nice, but not necessarily something that would help you get the job done. Yet once you see it done well, and watch how it unlocks the patient's (or parent's) ability to help themselves, it's very convincing. The language that Sarah was using in Alyssa's room that morning was all this and more.

Motivational interviewing works well as a respectful and engaging dialogue that recognizes the active role a patient plays in wellness. In emotionally driven illness the situation is more complicated. Deep down, there is motivation to get better. But in emotionally driven symptoms the motivation to be well is sometimes very deep down, buried under a more desperate motivation to maintain the mantle of protection that the illness provides. This is where providers need at least the very basic MedPsych skills. Solidly grounded in the principles of MedPsych treatment, Sarah fully understood the nature of Alyssa's symptoms. Alyssa was having abdominal pain every time she sat down to a meal. She was getting headaches when it was time for group therapy. Sarah was able to honestly and convincingly say to Alyssa that she knew she was telling the truth about her pain. *And,* that we needed her to do the things we asked anyway.

Empathy and empowerment. Validation of how real the patient's experience of physical symptoms were. I clearly witnessed the power of this approach that morning with Alyssa and Sarah. I also felt the basic humanity in it. And I would see it over and over again. It was hard work responding to hostility and anger with nuanced reactions. But I was gathering up a host of tools to help me do just that.

Motivating communication was at the heart of what we did as a MedPsych team, but it was carried along by something more ephemeral than simple word choice. Alyssa and her family, like all new admissions to our unit, struggled in the beginning and threatened to leave on an almost daily basis. But they didn't leave. Due to some combination of growing insight and having very few options, they hung in there. Four weeks later Alyssa appeared much brighter in her mood, was eating with steadily diminishing abdominal pain, and was gaining weight and planning her future. I explained to the referring hospitalist back in Boston that she would be attending our MedPsych Partial program for a few weeks, where she would continue the kind of therapies we had offered in our Inpatient program while transitioning back to home, family life, and school.

Alyssa's pediatrician had been down a long, rough road with her. She was pleasantly surprised that Alyssa had made so much progress.

"What are you guys using over there?" the pediatrician asked with a chuckle. "Unicorn tears?"

In retrospect, confidence and optimism from the whole team seemed to be what carried us forward. I would learn that optimism born of experience was the secret ingredient that gave the MedPsych providers the strength and resilience we needed to tackle these daunting situations day after day, week after week. That optimism was well-earned. The success rate for the MedPscyh program was remarkable. I witnessed firsthand that if we could align with the patients and their families our approach would work. When meeting with a new patient I frequently heard Dan Spencer say "We believe we can help you. And we will hold hope for you until you can hold hope for yourself."

So yeah, unicorn tears.

─────── C H A P T E R I I ───────

Floating Lead Balloons

CARLA WAS A SIXTEEN-YEAR-OLD WHO CAME TO US FROM A nationally regarded medical center in New York. Her and her single mother had been struggling with Carla's "mysterious" physical symptoms for over a year. When she was fourteen years old she began experiencing numbness and tingling in her legs that had progressed to weakness over the previous two years, preventing her from standing or walking without support. It wasn't long before she felt unable to go to school.

Carla's long list of unrelated medical diagnoses defied logic not only in their variety and number, but also in the very key fact that many of them did not explain her symptoms. Yet these labels of chronic concussion, Lyme disease, refractory (not responding to treatment) migraines, irritable bowel syndrome, and more were the only guideposts the patient and family could see. The diagnoses may have felt validating, but they were not helpful. Treating Carla for these conditions offered no relief, and in fact she continued to decline. Labels in all aspects of

life, including medical labels, are seductive. They offer a sense of orga-
nization and direction in the midst of chaos. Carla's life had become
medical chaos.

The MedPsych team knew from preadmission phone interviews and
review of records that Carla's parents had divorced four years previously,
and Dad had not kept in touch with Carla. Her mother had struggled
with depression for years, and was in therapy. There were indications
that her father's angry temper was a significant feature of the marital
discord. Mom felt like she had to run interference for Carla with her
school and even her doctors. Over the past year, as the school offered
increasing accommodations to help Carla attend, Carla's mobility
steadily deteriorated to the point where she was not able to walk or even
sit up in a wheelchair without supports. She developed crushing headaches that made it impossible for her to lift her head off the pillow. Her
eating became very restrictive due to abdominal pain. The headache
now required her to spend the entire day in bed, in a dark, quiet room.

We learned that Carla had a younger brother who was athletic, pop-
ular, and excelled academically, but he had grown more distant and
irritable over the past year. He was recently suspended from school for
fighting. The divorced parents could barely control their need to point
fingers at each other for the current state of their family. Dad refused to
participate in family therapy.

Carla had several hospital admissions in New York. Our review of
her mountain of medical records documented the extensive evaluations,
treatments, medication trials, and rehabilitative services that offered no
answers or improvements, only further decline. Diagnosis after diagnosis was added to the list. Nothing was removed. Carla's mom, desperate
and frightened, was finally persuaded by one of the specialists to have
Carla admitted to our program.

Carla's therapeutic plan felt as steady as a drumbeat to me. As proposed to the family in advance of admission we would focus on improving her function while offering intense emotional support. We knew to
expect that this would be an unwelcome shift for patient and parents

alike. We were emphasizing what we would ask Carla to do, as opposed to what we were going to do *to* her or *for* her. In some ways we were like a tender, supportive boot camp. The therapeutic goal in the beginning would be simply to get out of bed every morning. She would be expected to get to the nurse's station for her meds and the group room for her meals. She would ultimately be expected to come to all scheduled activities. Carla, we emphasized, needed to show up no matter how awful her illness was making her feel. This was as pleasant a prospect to MedPsych patients as the idea of getting an abscess on your leg drained with an eighteen-gauge needle. It was also just as necessary and effective.

We also emphasized and reemphasized that we were not going to pursue further medical diagnoses. We would accept all the evaluations and results done previously, and not repeat them or consider new diagnoses unless something changed clinically. I assured them there would be close medical monitoring by the Pediatric staff. The MedPsych team was confident that the camouflage of diagnoses would lose its relevance for Carla and her family by the sheer power of restoring her function in a setting of strong therapeutic support and intense emotional work.

We had been over all this in the preadmission phone conversations and we heard then, just as we were hearing on her admission, many protests of "But she can't do that," or, from Carla herself, "This isn't going to work." Dan and Sarah emphasized how the staff would help Carla every step of the way, with compassion and a full understanding of the illness. This part would usually go over like a lead balloon. Whether or not the family remained in the program would depend on which way the scales tipped: On one side, all that parental instinct screaming at them to protect and accommodate their suffering child, and on the other side, not only the horror that Carla's monstrous illness had robbed her of a normal life, but also the realization that Hasbro MedPsych was their only remaining option. We would do our best to tip those scales with our conviction and our hopefulness. That usually carried some weight. Despite her considerable misgivings, Carla's mother agreed—for the moment—that they would explore the emotional core of this illness.

There was a lot of work to be done. Carla had been on a daily regimen that included more than twenty prescription and over-the-counter medications. Many of them were redundant. Most of them had side effects. Few of them seemed to actually help anything. This was typical of many of our patients when they first arrived on our unit. At the same time the patient and family were hesitant to give up any of them—also very typical. MedPsych illness means the family is up to their eyeballs in uncertainty and false hopes. Their instincts are telling them to shut the windows and lock the doors, not to open things up to fresh air and sunlight. Reducing Carla's medication list by working with Hasbro's Pain and Palliative Care team was just that: fresh air and sunlight. Our plans to gradually streamline her medications would be another of many lead balloons we sent the family's way.

Carla's mother was, as expected, still worried that there was a medical explanation that we were all missing. She was terrified about Carla's profound deterioration. Carla's mother in particular continued to believe that mild irregularities in past nonspecific lab tests held the key, and Carla echoed every point her mother made, but with more hostility. They were both desperate and at the same time they were sort of stuck with us.

At this point in my tenure on the MedPsych unit I could quickly recognize the loss of function, accommodation, treatment resistance, and alteration of family dynamics amidst Carla's striking but distracting physical symptoms. The hallmarks of emotionally based medical illness were bouncing off the walls of Carla's room. She had a very complex disorder with extreme functional deficits in her mobility, her nutrition, and her social/educational development, all due to the pain and discomfort her symptoms caused. She was in a wheelchair because of her perceived weakness. Paralysis is a neurologic condition, so this aspect of her illness represents functional neurologic disorder. Her headache and abdominal pain represent somatic symptom disorder.

It is useful to return to Eleanor and Mike here, in order help us put Carla's illness in perspective.

Eleanor, our little friend from my previous primary care practice, suffered from abdominal pain as her primary symptom. This was also one of Carla's complaints. But Eleanor's illness was much less intense and more easily treated. Eleanor's condition earned the term "somatization" rather than somatic symptom disorder, which implies a more entrenched form of bodily symptoms. This is in contrast to Mike's illness which mimicked seizures. Seizures are a neurologic condition and therefore Mike was diagnosed with functional neurologic disorder. Carla's motor deficits mimic a neurologic disorder. So Carla's much more complex presentation involved both somatic and FND features.

The types of symptoms and the level of debilitation varied widely amongst these three patients, yet they presented with those same four diagnostic features at varying levels of intensity: loss of ability to function at their previous age-typical level, stubborn treatment resistance, accommodations by the adults in their lives, and altered family dynamics. Just as importantly, these very different presentations of emotionally based illness all responded to the same general principles of treatment: provide psychoeducation about emotionally based illness, and restore function in a setting of emotional support.

CHAPTER 12

The Fever of Emotion

D R. MICHELLE RICKERBY, A LEGENDARY CHILD PSYCHIA-
trist and instructor in the MedPsych program, talked to our
team frequently about how we often had to push families and
patients into distress in order to flush out the hidden emotional culprit.
What does that look like? It doesn't mean we are creating emotional
turmoil. The turmoil is already there, under many layers and wearing all
manner of disguises. We just slowly challenge the myths and withdraw
the accommodations to the illness that have allowed the patient's emotional illness to flourish.

In Carla's case "pushing her into distress" meant setting functional
expectations for her that were typical for a girl her age. We would give
her lots of support—physical and emotional—and incentivize that with
positive reinforcements like access to electronic devices when she was
able to comply. But no matter what we did on our end, the real work
would sit with Carla. We knew going into this that she would be quite
alarmed and very angry with us at first. The parents, seeing this, would
panic at our lack of understanding. There had never been a medical

explanation for why she didn't tolerate foods by mouth, or why she had lost so much mobility, and yet this debilitating illness had produced the strong belief that her body was failing her.

Emotionally driven illness is a tenacious overlord. Over and over again we witnessed how patients and families will do anything to avoid the inevitable distress that awaits them if we challenge the illness. No matter how realistic a picture of our program we tried to paint for them in all the conversations leading up to this admission, what Carla's mother primarily focused in on was our optimistic conviction that we could help her. Exhausted and frightened, like almost all the parents and patients who arrived at our doors, they were gravely disappointed to see our approach in action: demedicalizing their very vulnerable child. It meant lots of psychoeducation for Carla and her parents. It meant advancing an oral diet with the help of a dedicated team of dieticians and a brilliant speech and language therapist who had specific expertise in oral motor function. It meant calling upon our remarkable physical and occupational therapists to guide the patient back to appropriate mobility and self-care. It meant pulling in the Pain and Palliative Care team to help Carla manage her pain rather than cover it up. It meant expecting Carla to interact with peers, and talk about feelings. It meant doing everything that this illness was trying to avoid.

Both the parents and the treatment team need to tolerate all the pushback and distress that comes with a therapeutic plan. Carla's mother insisted at first that she could not tolerate oral food and that we were moving too fast. Mom worried she was too weak to move around the unit on her own, pointing out that she had not been able to get out of bed before noon for months. They also argued that she simply could not tolerate daylight through the window, or the noises of the other patients on the unit. When a weekly rhumba class, complete with energetic music, was set up just outside her room, her mother became so audibly agitated that we ushered her off the unit to a quiet space so we could talk it out. The behavioral health providers—the psychiatrists and psychologists—handle this kind of distress the way a pediatrician handles fever. Sure it feels terrible, but more importantly, it alerts us to the presence of illness and even helps suppress the infection. I would never achieve the same appreciation for emotional distress as I did for fever, but I sure came to understand its usefulness.

This expected and necessary experience of distress is a big part of why parental presence is a requirement for acceptance into our program. Ideally, both parents are there but if not, the one who can't be is expected to join in family meetings remotely. As Carla's family illustrates, MedPsych illness is a family illness. Concerned for their daughter, the divorced parents fully agreed to our plan from three thousand miles away. Just as predictably they recoiled from the realities of the plan once it was clear we were actually going to carry it out. Carla's distress at having her symptoms challenged turned up the volume of treatment resistance in all their heads. *These doctors have the wrong impression,* the illness tells them. *They don't realize how sick Carla really is. They don't know what they are doing. Coming here was a terrible mistake.*

I gently reiterated in subsequent family encounters that we would not be doing more lab tests or revisiting previously ruled out medical diagnoses. We would not accept her dietary restrictions unless we saw evidence of an intolerance. Our proposed plan could always be adjusted if clinically indicated, but that would be a medical decision, not an attempt to lower Carla's distress.

As the first week of Carla's admission progressed, it became clear to all parties that Carla was suffering with a severe loss of function. The psychological purpose it served was not yet apparent, and the family was still skeptical about our focus on emotional aspects. It also became apparent that there had been a long history of family-wide dysfunction. There was still a lot to be unpacked. Our therapeutic plan, as expected, produced far more distress than relief.

A key component of Carla's plan was that we would expect her to attend the "milieu" activities every day. In psychological context, "milieu" refers to the therapeutic atmosphere that the patient will be participating in. It can be highly structured, as is the case for the very ill children on the MedPsych unit, where just about every activity the patient participates in throughout the day is, at its heart, therapeutic. Or it can be the child's home and family life for a child such as Eleanor whose parents, through their informed decisions and guidance, provide the therapeutic support that she needs to get back in school.

Most of our patients start out highly resistant to participation in the milieu and Carla was no exception. Staff would encourage her to get out of bed and ready for the day, and fortunately they were remarkably successful at getting the teens to do things they initially refused to do.

The staff would not use physical force. Physical force was only used in the case of keeping a patient safe from imminent danger. Refusing to get out of bed or to sit in front of a breakfast tray with peers does not pose imminent danger. But at some point we might have to draw a line in the sand.

"If you refuse to comply with the basic plan you agreed to on admission, then this is not the program for you."

Patients, who have the legal right to leave the program at any time, might initially see that as a ticket home, but parents, seeing us as the last resort, would usually find the inner strength to insist to the child that she stay. This in fact was part of therapy: parents reclaiming a healthy parental role. They needed to understand that what they had to do in order to help Carla was to stop giving the illness everything it was demanding, even though that would cause them all a great deal of distress. They had to be on board—at least in Carla's presence—with expecting her to get out of bed, and to work on eating by mouth. Just as importantly, they had to be able to tolerate the anger and distress that this shift would trigger in Carla. For Carla, this was a monstrous betrayal. She was terrified of the team's plan, and stunned that her parents were not protecting her anymore.

For our plan to be successful, our multidisciplinary team needed to remain steady amidst all this feverish swirl of emotion. Carla's physical and occupational therapists showed up every day, armed with kindness, persistence, and godlike skills. The speech and language therapist managed her feeding rehabilitation and never seemed to lose her patience. I was always impressed by the degree of playfulness they all brought to their tasks—bringing in some teen magazines that Carla could look at between swallowing attempts, or getting clearance for Carla to watch a silly video while working through the painful abdominal reaction to having food in her stomach.

The dieticians outlined a plan for nutritional recovery and updated us in rounds every morning on what she was eating and what she was avoiding, as well as their observations on her mindset and attitudes. Our pain specialist, Dr. Angie Anderson, gradually whittled away at Carla's two-page med list, listening carefully to Carla and her parents with her signature compassion and humor. Her recommendations for integrative modalities, such as the yoga and massage therapies her team offered, came wrapped in an infectious enthusiasm that instilled hope in whoever was in the room—patient, family, or doctor.

Carla and her family weren't the only ones who benefitted from all this collaboration. In addition to the dietician report in rounds every morning, I would meet with them and the Eating Disorder team weekly to discuss the nutritionally impaired patients in depth. Dr. Donaldson, who headed the Eating Disorder team, would share her experience and wisdom with us like it was honey dripping from a hive. When the second pediatrician, Linda Doberstein, joined our team a few years into my tenure, I was able to step back in these meetings and fully appreciate as an observer what a gift it was for a pediatrician to have regular, direct access to so many experts in so many domains. Becoming competent in MedPsych work did not mean that Linda or I acquired all this expertise. It meant we had a more complete understanding of what all these experts could do, and how knowing that made us so much more effective in our own interactions with the patient.

Collaboration and expertise aside, I would come to expect that this was slow, slow work. It was one-step-backwards-for-every-two-steps-forward kind of work. By definition, no one who does MedPsych work—not the core treatment team and not the ancillary specialists—requires a lot of instant gratification.

It is important to keep in mind that the MedPsych program is completely voluntary. Patients can leave whenever they want. In Rhode Island that meant that legally the patient didn't even need parental consent, despite their age. And yet although families threatened to "yank" their kids out on a regular basis, and patients generally demanded it on an hourly basis, it didn't actually happen very often. In those first few weeks we worked hard to support the parents in getting Carla to agree to the treatment. We knew to expect that the patient's symptoms would likely escalate over the first few days of admission as the illness shouted down any talk of recovery. Navigating this frustrating path that would move Carla forward in the face of treatment resistance would be a daily dance. It quickly became clear to me that there is no such thing as treating an emotional illness without causing emotional distress.

MedPsych work reshaped my very concept of the doctor-patient relationship, instilling it with a new humility about what we could do and what we should do. This treatment approach was not about convincing other people to do what you thought was best for them, or their children. They had to decide that change was needed and be the agents of that change. Once they grasped, with our support, that they could be those agents, (week three?) most parents took that and ran with it.

I also realized, looking back, that a lot of outpatient pediatric treatment worked that way as well. There were times when I could have dialed back my medical "rightness" and accepted where the family was at that moment. I certainly wish I could have tolerated parents' distress a little better, and recognized the emotional fever that swirled around emotionally based illnesses as the diagnostic and potentially therapeutic presence that it was.

CHAPTER 13

A Language of Hope

EXTREMELY CHALLENGING PATIENTS LIKE CARLA PROVIDE an excellent classroom in which to hone communication skills. I was already learning the nuanced art of motivational dialogue. I was growing more confident in recognizing the dynamics of transference and countertransference that can so quickly derail a therapeutic encounter. I understood why my therapeutic messaging demanded carefully chosen words that coordinated smoothly with what the patient was hearing from the rest of the team. What I did not expect to get hung up on was conjunctions.

I teased the psychiatrists about their avoidance of the word "but." They avoided it with patients, in therapy, in team discussions, and even in administrative meetings. So when an annoyed sixteen-year-old pronounced that Dr. Spencer did not know what he was talking about and he needed to get the hell out of her room, she heard in response from Dan:

"I'm glad you're being honest. It's important to us to know how you feel. *And* (my italics represent the vocal inflection here) we really believe that our plan will help you reach your goals."

I would sit there in those early sessions with a mix of curiosity and skepticism, trying consciously *not* to raise one know-it-all eyebrow at the nitpicking semantics, and wondering how the heck that was any different than saying what I would have likely said: "Well, I'm glad you're being honest, *but* we know from experience that this will work."

There were so many more words to trip over than *ifs, ands,* and *buts.* Once I had begun to settle into my role on the unit, Dan, the treating psychiatrist on Carla's team, suggested I run a discharge planning meeting with Carla and her family. This was an encouraging show of confidence. Discharge planning required so much more than discussing the pediatric issues. The whole team would be at the meeting, but I would steer the agenda. In order to do that well I would need to have a full, integrated picture of all the work done by all the specialties involved in Carla's care, and be able to verbally shape all that input into a cohesive discharge plan.

By this point Carla had been on our unit for two months. She had recently started walking independently after needing a wheelchair for almost a year prior to admission. She had aligned with our physical and occupational therapists and our feeding specialist and was making steady gains not only in her mobility but in her oral feeding as well. It was time for her to transition to a less restrictive level of care. All parties had agreed she was ready to step down to the MedPsych Partial program.

I had a lot to cover in the discharge meeting. The intermediary plan to having Carla return home was for her to attend the MedPsych day program while living as an outpatient at the Ronald McDonald House. Patients and their families are usually quite anxious at this point in recovery, and transitions are almost always rocky. We expect regression. No team member at that meeting was surprised when Carla asked why she wouldn't be allowed to use a wheelchair at the Partial program. She asked this despite the fact that she hadn't used a wheelchair in a week.

"Couldn't I have it there just in case I need it?"

I offered a pretty good explanation of the therapeutic reasoning behind not bringing the wheelchair, and was confident that I had stayed on message.

"We know now that your body can walk, and that it's your illness telling your body it is weak," I said, and I reminded her in detail of the tremendous progress she had made.

I then summed up my response with a common phrase.

"We don't want to set you up for failure by providing equipment we know you don't need."

Carla and her mother both gave a slight twitch of their heads and looked a little concerned, but overall it felt like a good meeting, and I left satisfied that we had done a good job of preparing this family for the next level of care. I was really getting the hang of this.

A few minutes later there was a light knock on my office door, and Dan walked in.

"That was great," he said. "You did a really nice job. I can tell you're going to be good at this."

I really liked Dan. He had such a gentle manner. And how nice was this that he came over to my office to offer me encouragement? What I didn't immediately see was that this was the start of a "feedback sandwich." Say positive things, then follow that with more encouragement.

"You did a great job of reminding Carla why she wouldn't be using a wheelchair at Partial."

I could hear the "*but*" coming in my head. As far as I was concerned, it was going to be the equivalent of a "*but*," even if he didn't say it. He took a pause instead of a conjunction and then went straight to a new sentence without any ifs, ands, or buts. I have to admit, it worked. Whatever he was going to say next didn't diminish the praise he had just offered.

"I would like to make a comment on one thing you said."

"Okay."

"You said you didn't want to set them up for failure. 'Failure' is a pretty loaded, negative term, especially for our patients, who tend to feel very unsure about themselves at this point. I think both Carla and her mother reacted a bit to that word. The most important thing we offer our patients is hope. And we really are very hopeful that she will do well in Partial. That's what we focus on. If she regresses we know that is a predictable course of recovery and we can support her through that. It's not failure. We really are not expecting failure. Can you see the difference in the two ways I said that?"

I could not. At least not in that moment. It all seemed so overly self-conscious. What I was thinking—defensively—was "You've got to be kidding me."

What I actually said was, "But doesn't that mean the same thing? Don't they know it means the same thing?"

I could feel my face crease with confused frustration as I stared at the space above Dan's head. Dan just sat there and looked at me with a friendly expression, not saying anything else. Another remarkable thing about psychiatrists and psychologists is that they are so comfortable not saying anything. That always amazed me. It even made me feel uncomfortable for them when I witnessed it. I am a verbal gap filler. Always have been. Now I can see how that can be a communication problem in itself. I'm pretty sure my "we don't want to set you up for failure" was one of those gap fillers.

"Okay," I finally said after a few deep breaths. I really was thrown off, not just by this particular incident but by the realization that there seemed to be a million ways to say something wrong in this job.

"But," I continued (and I don't believe he corrected me) "you're going to have to keep helping me with this. It's like I need to learn a whole new language."

"And you will," he answered with his usual positivity. "You're already doing great. We're very lucky to have you."

The sandwich was complete, and I witnessed, as I did many times in this job, that a formulaic approach to dialogue did not have to exclude authenticity and warmth.

Fortunately, Dan patiently stayed on message with me those first few months, with frequent good-natured reminders. So, when I chimed in during a leadership meeting, "I know the milieu therapists are getting frustrated but I really need them to do this," Dan grinned that grin of his and offered "*Aaand* you really need them to do this."

I remember remarking to another psychiatrist after a somewhat contentious administrative meeting "So you can say 'shit' in a meeting. You just can't say 'but.' Do I have that right?"

She smiled and replied in a congratulatory tone, "That's right!"

It didn't take long for me to catch on, mostly because I experienced firsthand that word choice really did make a difference in how well we aligned with the patient. In fact the whole issue made me aware of just how often in the course of a day we use "and" or "but," or unconsciously choose a negative slant like avoiding failure rather than a positive one of preparing for success. If a word choice has even the most nuanced of impact, the very frequency of occurrence in our dialogue magnifies its significance. The guy fixing my muffler probably doesn't notice or care about "ands" and "buts," but the more personal the conversation is, and the more vulnerable the person you are talking too, the more critical this kind of dialogue is. I came to recognize that for doctors "and" and "but" are some of the most powerful and yet overlooked words we use.

These language choices may be subtle but that doesn't mean that patients (or their parents) need to be sentence-diagramming linguists to benefit from our word choice. As I listened carefully to Dan or Sarah or the other seasoned therapists talk to patients, I could indeed hear how "and" is much more likely to convey to a family that you are actively listening to what is being said and can validate it. "But" is much more likely to convey that you are dismissing or invalidating the speaker's point of view in favor of your own.

Somewhere deep in the language centers of all of us—yes, even the sleepy-eyed thirteen-year-old who can't remember where he left his socks—is a kind of human sonar that recognizes this language of validation and trust and alignment, even if that barefoot listener can't quite identify what specifically left him with that positive impression. The result, as I saw play out over and over in loaded conversations, was not trivial. *And,* I would need a lot more practice before it became second nature to me.

It turned out there were countless other communication minefields in the MedPsych world that went well beyond semantics. You can hear them anywhere, of course. But there is so much more at stake when you are trying to help someone in extreme emotional pain.

I put it to use shortly after that talk with Dan. I met Jackie who, among other issues, was struggling with an eating disorder that she was adamantly denying. Jackie insisted that eating anything but a few vegetables at dinner provoked food allergies that caused severe swelling of her tongue and throat. Her emotional brain generated a somatic symptom—the sensation of a swollen tongue and throat—to support her overpowering need to restrict food. I had reviewed all her medical records pertaining to possible allergies or GI disorder, and was working closely with the dieticians and the Eating Disorder team to safely meet her nutritional needs. In a strong response of treatment resistance, Jackie was thrusting her tongue out in bizarre ways during meals, and complaining of shortness of breath whenever she felt pressured to eat. I told the team I would meet with her.

I began our encounter a little differently than I might have in my previous practice.

"It sounds like this has been a pretty rough day for you. It must be hard to get stomach pain every time you swallow a bite of food."

I understood now that her experience of symptoms was real, and I knew better than to say "*but* that doesn't sound like food allergies to me. I think it's your anxiety." All my energy was being funneled into restoring function in a supportive way. That's where the money is. So no "buts," no diagnoses. I praised Jackie for eating what she could that day and considered what goals we shared. I reviewed how increasing the volume of food in her stomach was making her GI muscles work harder—just like a runner's calves will ache if she hasn't been running for a while. I knew that a frame of "getting into shape" would likely appeal to her. I had to walk a fine line between that and a focus on calorie burning, which is a common feature of eating disorders. Therapeutic language was often a tightrope. It took practice, and I often slipped.

I looked for other positive developments to report to Jackie, like her improved potassium level. I validated her feelings and reactions wherever I could, and chose positive language as quickly as I could come up with it.

"Your heart rate is coming up and your BP is more stable. You're doing a great job of taking care of yourself, even when it hurts."

Every sentence, every medical term, every validation, every topic I avoided in these conversations were the result of an informed choice on my part rather than a reaction to what her illness or my unhelpful biases were trying to say. At first, this all made my brain hurt. I was an experienced pediatrician who had grown accustomed to having medical conversations slip off my tongue with practiced ease. Yet now in this MedPsych role there were moments when I found myself stammering through explanations like a third-year medical student.

Jackie gradually responded to our program's intense psychological support. She still struggled with eating, but the initial focus on allergic symptoms started to fade into the background. There was other functional progress as well. She was making meaningful connections with a few of her peers, having more honest conversations with her parents, and recognizing when she was anxious and what triggered it. She was able to tolerate a varied diet without anxiety or resistance. Just as significantly she was able to eat in the presence of her peers and her family, and could be distracted by the conversation at the table, rather than obsessing on what she was putting in her mouth. Obviously all this didn't happen because I was able to parse a sentence on the fly, but it was clear that I had expanded my communication skill set and that moved all of us forward. It was a skill set that would have significantly enriched my previous outpatient practice. If only.

Just as interesting as the effect word choice has on a patient encounter is the impact it can have on our own behaviors and therapies. Like a self-fulfilling prophecy, when we say we are "redirecting" a patient rather than punishing or reprimanding them, we actually tend to redirect rather than punish or reprimand.

For example, Liz might get a reminder.

"That's inappropriate language for the unit, Liz."

More expletives follow.

"Do you need to take a walk around the unit?" or

"What coping skills have you been working on in therapy?" or

"Do you want to try a squeeze ball?"

Shifting the spotlight can help too:

"Who saw the hedgehog from the zoo today?"

As any confident classroom teacher can tell you, none of this works perfectly all the time, but I was very impressed with how often it really did work, especially in a patient who had been in our therapeutic milieu for two or three weeks. Young people, even the most troubled, yearn to be able to direct their own lives. I was always a little surprised to see how often a distressed teen was able to regroup in response to suggestions for self-management rather than a complaint about his behavior. The exchange provided the patient a chance to take another small step towards being the self-directed person they wanted to be. A hammer coming down on a head could never cultivate that.

Imagine how different the interaction would look if we allowed ourselves to talk about *making* the patients do things, or *not tolerating* these behaviors. There seems to be a natural human inclination to reach for these controlling kinds of terms when we are frustrated by another's behavior—especially a child's or teen's. I occasionally heard this kind of language pop up in rounds or other clinical team meetings, especially if the staff person was new or "floating" from another unit in the hospital. *And* we would *redirect* our colleagues in the same respectful way.

Words like "incentives" and "disincentives" are another example of this. They imply that behaviors rely to a significant degree on patient choice, not staff control. Then there's *preferred* rather than *favorite*. The first recognizes the human reality that we get along with some personalities better than others. Nothing wrong with that. *Favorite* is dicier, as it opens up the door to drama, manipulation, exclusion—all the kinds of maladaptive behaviors that can trip teens up. When Jackie declared that she wanted that nice Dr. Doberstein to be her pediatrician rather than that awful Dr. Kozel, I was able to reach into my handy new toolkit. It took a little practice, but honestly, just a little. Once you realize how much impact it has on a doctor-patient interaction, it becomes your language of choice.

"I understand you may not like me very much right now. I get it. I'm glad to hear that there are staff here that you feel more comfortable with and will confide in when you're upset. *Aaand* we need to find a way to work together."

It takes a small army of mental health workers, nurses, and therapists to maintain this intense round-the-clock therapeutic atmosphere on the milieu. The same basic concepts and the language tools that support MedPsych patients are equally useful to pediatricians in outpatient practice as we model this approach on a scaled-back level for our patients with less intense emotionally driven illnesses.

I imagine how my conversation with Eleanor at that outpatient visit would have changed.

"We know your tummy really hurts, and we also know that it is important to get back to school, even when your tummy hurts. We know being sick makes you sad. This is how you get better."

── CHAPTER 14 ──

Pride and Prejudice

WORKING WITH ADOLESCENTS MEANS ACKNOWLEDG-
ing their sexuality. There's no getting around it. We are
sexual beings from the moment we are born, and as chil-
dren approach puberty their sexuality plays a greater and greater role in
their sense of self. If there is confusion or shame or trauma around one's
sexuality during this critical developmental transition, we can expect
that there will also be significant emotional suffering. A homosexual or
transgender child growing up in a family that does not accept the child's
reality may experience a great deal of anxiety as he or she or they reaches
adolescence. To be clear, the child's suffering will not be due to their
experience of sexuality. It will be due to a rejection of their very sense of
self by the people they love and depend on. Young human psyches are
simply not designed to withstand that kind of assault on their self-iden-
tity and attachments.

It is not at all surprising that in a hospital unit full of adolescents,
sexuality is a common focus of assertion and discussion. That's really
not so different than what gets discussed at a sleepover or in a locker

room. But the teens that were admitted to the MedPsych program were struggling with emotional distress that was too overwhelming for them to consciously manage. It is not surprising to find that for some of our patients that emotional tidal wave was the result of struggling in secret with their sexual orientation or gender, terrified of acknowledging it even to themselves.

Kevin was a sixteen-year-old from New Jersey who was part of a large, loving, conservative Christian family. He was the oldest of seven children, all of whom were homeschooled. He played football on a local high school team for one season, but other than that had little contact with teens outside his church community. He understood homosexuality to be a sin.

Two years prior to admission Kevin developed photophobia—an intolerance of light. He required dimmer and dimmer ambient lighting in order to avoid the severe eye pain and headaches it triggered. He wore sunglasses indoors and out, except when he was sleeping. His family brought him to numerous ophthalmological and neurological specialists, but all the exams, scans, and imaging studies failed to turn up any abnormality. As he spent more and more time in his darkened bedroom he grew isolated and depressed. His parents were frantic. His church rallied around him, providing spiritual and practical supports. The family was eventually convinced by a trusted physician to seek help in our program.

There were many challenges to bringing Kevin into our program. Family-based treatment is a cornerstone of the MedPsych treatment approach. No child experiences emotional illness in a vacuum, and parental presence is a requirement for admission to our program. But there were six younger children at home and Kevin's mother felt unable to be with him full-time in Providence. His father was worried about how much work he could afford to miss. Eventually, with the help of other church members, Mom and Dad were able to take turns being present in our program while the other parent joined our meetings by phone.

When Kevin first presented to our emergency room for a scheduled admission, I went down to meet him, as was my usual procedure. I was very surprised, however, to see him in a wheelchair. My role in the pre-admission process was to review the patient's functional abilities in all domains. Neurologic and nutritional domains were top of the list. So was mobility. Nobody was supposed to show up in our program in a wheelchair without us knowing about it and therapeutically planning for it. So after a quick round of introductions I asked Kevin why he was in the wheelchair. He looked at his mother and his mother did the talking.

"We noticed over the last few days, just as we were getting ready to come up here, he started losing his balance. He's very wobbly now without this," she said, holding up a cane. "We were hoping there is a specialist here who can tell us what's going on."

Part of me was relieved to hear that I hadn't missed a really important detail of his illness. Another part of me drew a deep breath at the realization that this was the most treatment resistance I had ever seen before we even made it out of the ER. I realized just how terrified Kevin must have been to show up here. As we traversed the six floors in the patient elevator, I made pleasant small talk with Kevin and his mom, but my mind was spinning in another direction. *What's my next step?*

As we stepped off the elevator for the sixth floor, Jen Larose, the nurse manager, was waiting for us with her great signature smile. Fortunately, she knew exactly what the next step was. She did a double take when she first saw the wheelchair and then tilted her head at me with an even broader "isn't this interesting?" kind of smile. Then she spotted the cane in Mom's arm and gently reached for it.

"I'll just keep this in my office for now," she said matter-of-factly but still smiling.

"Oh, he's going to need that," Kevin's mother said.

Jen did that head-tilting, wide-grinning thing at me again to let me know I would have some explaining to do, and then turned back to Mom.

"So this is a safety issue," she explained in her friendly manner. "We don't allow anything on the unit that might be used unsafely. I'm going to call Physical Therapy right now so they can come up and do an assessment."

And then, turning to Kevin she added kindly, "Don't worry. Our PT folks are great. They will make sure you have everything you need and are using your equipment properly."

We all proceeded through the double doors onto the unit. I introduced Kevin's nurse to him and his mother, and then headed to my office to regroup. This little snafu about Kevin's mobility and reliance on a cane wouldn't get as much as an eyebrow raise on any other floor of the hospital. However, MedPsych illness thrives by being a moving target. When one symptom is addressed, another more dramatic one appears. The path to success for our patients includes the pediatricians going over the medical histories and particularly the functional losses with a fine-tooth comb. That was the only way to create a cohesive therapeutic plan that could start on day one. And, as Jen so rightly pointed out, we also needed to make sure that whatever equipment is being used on the unit is not a safety hazard for the patient or others.

I found my colleague Linda at her desk in our shared office. Linda wouldn't miss the dot on an "i" in a medical record, and she had carefully reviewed Kevin's condition.

"Linda, do you remember reading or hearing anything about Kevin needing a cane or a wheelchair at home?"

"No," she answered. "He has no mobility issues. Why?"

And then, half a beat later, "Oh no. He does now?"

We would need to gather up the rest of the team before they left for the day so that we would all be on the same page about what assistive devices we would allow Kevin to use in our program when we convened for his family meeting the next morning.

Kevin meanwhile isolated himself in his room, lying on his bed with his sunglasses on. His mother was a little unnerved by some colorful language that was drifting in from the common area, but otherwise was holding up pretty well. Jesse, his physical therapist, had him back to bearing weight and walking in a matter of days. Over the next few weeks both Kevin and his parents really warmed to the physical and occupational therapists, and Kevin looked forward to their sessions. He bantered good-naturedly with the nursing and mental health staff, and started to form cautious friendships with a few of the other patients. Before long he had weaned off his sunglasses, and was moving confidently around the unit. He earned a trip off the unit with his parents to attend services at a nearby church. Kevin was all set to step down to the Partial program when he disclosed during an individual therapy session that he was gay.

The team's reaction was what it always was on issues of sexuality (and, for that matter, on almost any kind of issue.) We affirm what the patient is telling us. There is no reason to doubt him or to cross-examine him to make sure the assertion is "real." The critically important, compassionate, and therapeutic message was that we believed him and supported him. If he later had second thoughts or was confused, or panicked—whatever—we would accept that too. If a week from now or three years from now he questions his sexual orientation again, his doctors would need to affirm and support that while helping him to make sense of these experiences.

Kevin told his therapist that he had worried about being homosexual for several years. He knew his family and his wider church community considered that to be a horrendous sin, and would not accept it. So he kept trying to deny it to himself. It was the reason he quit football. It was the reason he isolated himself at home. He loved his family. He couldn't do this to them. He couldn't do it to God.

Pain came with this job. It was excruciating to watch the look on a transgender teen's face when their parents insisted on using the teen's birth name. It was heartbreaking to watch a parent dismiss a teen's revelation that they are gay. We would insist on affirming what their child was telling us, and use the name they had picked for themselves. I made frequent mistakes, calling a transgender patient by the name they came in with on admission, following that up with a grunt or other unpleasant vocalization at my mistake, apologizing and switching to their chosen name. And they would invariably be kind in return.

Our team discussed this new development with Kevin and brought it to the Partial team. We all agreed we would keep Kevin on the Inpatient unit a bit longer to help him be able to talk to his parents about this. The transition to the Partial program was challenging enough for our patients. Transitioning with a time bomb in their pocket was a bad idea all around.

A few days later, in an inspiring act of courage and with his therapist at his side for support, Kevin told his parents that he was gay. It did not go well. His mother burst into tears, and his father exploded—though not at Kevin, thankfully. All his anger was directed at us. He was angry at our program, at how we all "made my son gay." There was no acknowledgment of how much better Kevin was doing. He was now moving around fluidly without support and no longer avoided bright light. The sunglasses were tossed aside. We all got to appreciate his beautiful blue eyes.

My heart sank when his therapist recounted what happened in that session. By the time I heard the story Kevin was already gone, whisked back to the safety of New Jersey. He didn't have the chance to say goodbye to anyone. And we didn't have the chance to say goodbye to him. They had collected his belongings and signed the necessary paperwork in record time. At the last minute his nurse went running to find Jen. They wanted their cane back. It had been in the family for years.

This sad ending provides a reminder for all of us in the healthcare community. We know there are lots of anxious kids in our world, lots of family dysfunction, and lots of emotionally based physical symptoms. If you add to that mix kids who are keeping secrets about their sexuality—about their most basic sense of who they are—you are looking at some of the most vulnerable children out there. Healthcare providers already work hard to normalize discussions of sexuality with the families in their care, but even with us in those discussions we often assume heterosexuality and assigned gender as the starting point.

There are many ways to model open conversations for parents. A simple developmental question for a child in for their kindergarten physical, with Mom or Dad standing by, is "Are you a boy or a girl?" This will mostly trigger a cascade of giggles, but there will also be a response, followed sometimes by them asking me in a playful way, pointing at me, "Are *you* a boy or a girl?" And I would happily answer the most natural question on earth.

As a kiddo started puberty I would ask some version of "Do you like boys or girls?" Followed by, "You know you can ask your mom or dad anything about sex, right? About boys and girls? I mean, we all know it can get kind of confusing at times." That was as much a cue to the parents as it was advice to the child.

By the time my patients were old enough for me to see them without parents in the room I was much more direct about gender identification and orientation. I doubt I always got honest responses, but I could at least legitimize the questions.

It is critically important that we always affirm what a child is telling us about their sexual orientation or gender and urge parents to do the same. If a child or teen later modifies that assertion in any way we must listen and affirm that too, recognizing how complex a person's sexuality is. It's not like we just get one chance to figure out who we are. The only alternative is terrible suffering.

CHAPTER 15

Hubs Before Flubs

W E KNOW THAT EMOTIONALLY BASED ILLNESS THRIVES on accommodation. Significant adults in the child's life need to accommodate the child's loss of function, as in "Of course you can't go to school with these symptoms," in order for such an illness to survive. This role is usually supplied by the parents, but can also come from the misplaced generosity of school personnel. And sometimes it comes from well-meaning healthcare providers who are trying very hard not to alienate the family. Doctor's notes to excuse absences are a common example of this.

Lydia provides us with a hair-raising example of just how bad physician accommodation can get. MedPsych treatment is highly focused on emotional dynamics. But there is no question that the patient often suffers serious bodily harm from the medical evaluations and treatments that are first sought out.

Sixteen-year-old Lydia came to us from Pennsylvania, but not until after two years of seeking medical care up and down the East Coast regarding her chronic, persistent migraines. She was fourteen years old when the debilitating headaches started and hadn't been in school since. Lydia stayed at home all day with her mother. Her father had passed away when Lydia was a young child.

Lydia had been to multiple neurologists and pain clinics for her headaches. There were never any specific findings, and the concluding diagnosis was always the same: refractory (unresponsive to treatment) migraines. She underwent enough imaging studies to wallpaper a small house. I knew, because I had to review them all when we were considering her for admission. She had been prescribed opiates and benzodiazepines, a variety of migraine medicines and a mix of non-steroidal anti-inflammatory meds. Nothing helped. She was also advised to take many different vitamins and herbal supplements. Each new medication was added to the existing ones. Nothing was ever removed. Her medication list was two pages long.

All through this harrowing ordeal a giant red flag was waving in the background. Lydia was demonstrating one of the most cardinal features of MedPsych illness. The more aggressively she was treated for her unexplained symptoms, and the more medicines she was prescribed, the worse she got. Over the two-year period since leaving school, she went from hanging around the house all day watching videos and playing with her dog in the yard, to being bedridden in a dark room, protected from extraneous light or sound, refusing visitors or tutoring, and needing her mother's assistance to get to the bathroom.

What was most remarkable about her data-intense medical history and what was never mentioned by her mother or her previous providers was her dramatic weight loss. For all the time, money, and attention spent on looking for medical diagnoses to explain Lydia's inexplicable, devastating loss of function, nobody was talking about the one thing that could have actually killed her. Lydia was refusing to eat and everyone involved in her care up to that point seemed to be averting their eyes from that terrifying reality. It was not until she wheeled into our unit during a January blizzard that we learned she had been on a "hunger strike" for the past week. It turned out, as the story unfolded, it had been more like twelve weeks.

By the time Lydia arrived in our unit she had lost 15 percent of her last recorded body weight. That weight had been obtained months earlier and she had refused to be weighed since. She looked skeletal, her eyes dry and sunken. Her pulse was slow and her blood pressure low. She was literally starving.

This posed a dilemma for us. We could manage most medical issues as effectively as any other medical unit in the hospital, but our usual policy was that if you were sick enough to warrant medical (as opposed to psychiatric) admission you needed to be stabilized first on a medical floor before coming up to us. That was because we were not staffed the way the medical floors were, with round-the-clock hospitalists and pediatric residents on site. Pediatricians on the MedPsych unit were only there during the day. After hours, the nurses would have to pull in a doctor from the hospitalist service for any urgent matters.

At the same time, we understood how resistant Lydia and her mother were to treatment, and sending her off to a medical floor would almost certainly have resulted in them leaving against medical advice. The hospitalists could always bring down the hammer of an involuntary "hold" since she was so physically impaired, but that in turn would end any chance of us then being able to achieve a therapeutic alliance with the family. So we talked it over with the Eating Disorder team and the hospitalists and the chief resident, who oversaw the residents on call at night. We agreed on the next medical steps that we would carry out on our unit, including careful fluid resuscitation and cardiac monitoring, in collaboration with the Eating Disorder folks. Our intrepid nursing staff, all Med-Surg trained, were ready for the challenge. I would be the first call from home for anything short of a medical emergency. The hospitalist team, who agreed to round on her in our unit twice a day, would be ready to jump in if at any time they or we thought Lydia needed more intense intervention or monitoring. Fortunately she responded well to our stabilization efforts.

It was my job to explain to Lydia's mother why we were so quickly changing focus. Lydia's mom looked at me like I had two heads when I brought up the subject of Lydia's eating disorder.

"She doesn't have an eating disorder," said Mom with a confused look on her face. "She's just been really sick with migraines. Too sick to eat."

"She's starving to death, Mrs. _____," I said quietly, with as little drama as possible. But there was no room for diplomacy here, just as you don't tell a parent that their child with severe respiratory distress "may just need a little oxygen." Everyone needed to acknowledge how serious this was, and what could go wrong if we didn't intervene. I was stunned that this seemed like the first time she had heard this concern raised.

"So if it's that serious, why didn't any of her other doctors bring this up?" Mom asked with thinly veiled skepticism.

"I don't know," I answered truthfully. "But she is severely malnourished. Dangerously malnourished. Her potassium is low. Her heart rate is slower than it should be. We need to do tests to check how well her heart and liver are functioning. We need to monitor her electrolytes until they normalize. And we have to address all of this before we can address anything else."

Once the reality of the situation sank in it actually scared the living daylights out of Lydia's mom. In a display of courage that had been hidden under layer after layer of illness accommodations, she told her daughter that she needed slowly administered tube feedings until she was out of danger, and she insisted that Lydia comply. Lydia's psychologist Dr. Hagin and I stood by her for support. As Lydia released a frantic tirade of expletives and refusals, Mom shot us sidelong glances as if to say, "Well, she has a point." But we said nothing, just looked back at Mom with supportive demeanors, and out of that silence emerged their first therapeutic moment. Mom stood her shaky ground and told Lydia that she had to accept the refeeding plan. Pushed by sheer terror, Mom was taking control back from the illness on day one.

Predictably this early shift in the dynamics of the illness, with Mom able to take back the reins, terrified and angered Lydia. For the first few weeks I was the main target of that anger, since much of her emotional work had to be put on hold until she was medically stable. Lydia refused to talk to her mother about anything other than stopping the feedings and taking her back home.

I was learning to manage my frustration in these kinds of situations, but at the end of an exhausting day when a junior colleague had called in sick, again, and a disgruntled parent had complained about me to a hospital administrator, and I forgot to put in an order that the nurse had already asked for twice, I would have really appreciated a few minutes of goodwill. Lydia, on the other hand, was not in our program to support me. She was in a full-blown emotional fever, and although I did relieve that fever a bit by respecting her wishes and leaving the room sooner than I would have chosen to, my real job, along with that of everyone else on her treatment team, was to identify the source of that "fever" and expose it for what it was. We had already exposed the illness that was closest to the surface: the eating disorder. But we knew there were many more bad humors bubbling underneath that.

Lydia was with us for four long, exhausting months. By the time she was ready for the step-down program they had chosen near her home in Pennsylvania she was at a healthy weight, was complying with a structured meal plan, and participating constructively in therapy. She needed occasional migraine meds but took little else by way of pharmaceuticals.

The Lydia that emerged from MedPsych treatment was a kind, sensitive girl with a sharp intellect who loved to read fantasy fiction and sketch portraits of folks on the unit. That would have been hard to imagine when she was first admitted. She still had plenty of work to do, but now she also had dreams for her future—one of the best prognostic signs of all. I drove into the hospital early one Sunday morning to say goodbye to her. Lydia and her mom were catching an Amtrak back home. In an unprecedented display of physical contact, Lydia put her arms around me in a giant hug and thanked me.

Lydia's recovery was a slow but remarkable thing to witness. She was certainly the sickest patient we had ever accepted into our program, and I sure lost a lot of sleep that first week she was under my care. But it is important to not lose sight of the fact that before all those challenges and rewards our team experienced in caring for Lydia, she was almost killed with "kindness."

Lydia's story is a cautionary tale to all of us who find ourselves getting caught up in the web of emotionally based illness. We have to stick to the facts. Her PCP and the specialists she referred Lydia to could not find any explanation for her extreme symptoms. Certainly none of them had ever seen migraines cause a teen to be chronically bedridden, unable to even toilet themselves. And the more Lydia inexplicably sank into the pillows in her dark room, the more her doctor's reaction was to sympathize, accommodate, run more tests and use stronger and stronger meds in a downward spiral that is so typical of undiagnosed emotionally based illness.

Accommodation by others is one of the hallmark ingredients for MedPsych illness. In an unfortunate perfect storm of good intentions on the part of Lydia's mother, PCP, and specialists, the adults in Lydia's life responded to her like she was a waif in a Dickens novel. Her PCP even made house calls once Lydia appeared too sick to get out of bed. She encouraged Lydia to try and eat, and urged her to at least drink supplements, still believing Lydia when she said her food refusal was due to migraine pain. She was again admitted to a children's hospital so another neurologist could be consulted. He drew the very different conclusion that this was an extremely entrenched somatic symptom disorder and insisted that Lydia come to our program. Unfortunately, throughout all this effort, no one mentioned that Lydia was starving.

I knew I had to take some responsibility for this mess. When I asked how Lydia was eating, I was told by the very nice hospitalist on the other end that Lydia's pain and the narcotics she required had suppressed her appetite. When I asked for a recent weight, Dr. Nice told me Lydia was refusing to be weighed. When I asked them to fax me a growth curve, the most recent weight listed was from two years previous. When I asked for the PCP records, I was again mystified that there were so few office visits. It was mostly phone records regarding referrals to specialists or a need for med refills. If this had been a parent giving me the information,

I would have known to set some limits. I would have said we could not accept Lydia to our program until more complete information was provided. But I had never had to deal with such accommodating providers before. That mistake brought a critically ill teen to our doorstep.

All I can say in my defense is that I never made that mistake again. No recent weight data? No MedPsych program.

Over the first few days of Lydia's admission to our unit there was a small army of hospitalists, intensivists, eating disorder specialists, pain specialists, and pharmacists joining the MedPsych team in keeping Lydia from falling off the precarious cliff edge she was teetering on.

Lydia's tale, as extreme as it is, offers a cautionary tale for all healthcare providers. This level of provider accommodation was extreme to be sure. But we all must be on guard for whatever smaller accommodations we may be supplying. Many of us hear ourselves being a little too diplomatic when bringing up the subject of MedPsych symptoms, especially when the emotions in the exam room are already running high. Too often, specialists and PCPs alike feel like they have to build their case by ordering a slew of tests and not bringing up the messy topic of psychological factors until the third visit. Or even later.

Delay in necessary treatment isn't the only hazard that results. We know that the more diagnostic attention the physical symptoms get in an emotionally based disorder, the more convinced the family becomes that this is a medical condition.

I have been in that squirmy position of writing a note to excuse absences for a child who I was pretty sure had school-related anxiety. We think we are biding time to earn the parents' goodwill, or we are avoiding confrontation, or we are of the mindset that all other medical conditions should be ruled out before addressing the emotional component of the child's symptoms. Too often the child is referred to pediatric subspecialists before the PCP even considers addressing the school avoidance. All of that is misguided. It makes us part of the problem. And it's not just the school notes.

Do we, the PCPs, include in a specialist referral that we are concerned about school-related anxiety as the underlying issue? Or do we diplomatically write "Rule out seizure" and hope that the specialist will read between the lines?

Do we speak directly to the parents and child about the hallmarks of emotionally based illness and why that is highest on our list of differential diagnoses? Or do we gloss over that in an indirect way to avoid stirring up a lot of distress? Do we choose consultations and lab tests as a way of meeting families where they are, or simply to appease the parents?

I found it interesting that referrals to our program almost always came from subspecialists in large medical centers. When I would call the PCP to get their take on the patient and family, they almost always reported that they knew all along this was going to turn out to be an emotional issue. And I believed them. This foresight underscores the reality that PCPs, not specialists, are at the frontline, and we need to stay there. We need to be able to recognize and tolerate the distress that will surely roar up when we address the issue head-on. We cannot kick the can down the road. If we do feel subspecialty referral is indicated, we need to keep a close eye on what direction that can is rolling in. We need to communicate to the specialist that emotionally driven illness is at the top of our differential diagnosis. We need to always be on alert for all the ways emotionally based illness can pull us into its web.

Perhaps the most important lesson I took away from these experiences was that primary care providers need to be at the center of treatment for emotionally based symptoms. We need to recognize the cardinal features, educate families about it, and, very importantly, remain at the hub of the child's treatment. If we refer a patient to a specialist with our primary diagnosis being emotionally driven illness, then we need to make clear that that's what our primary diagnosis is, and frame our questions to the specialist along the lines of, "Do you think these symptoms warrant further investigation while we proceed with behavioral strategies?" That's not poisoning the well, even though the parents may see it that way. That is communication.

If a consultant feels other types of doctors need to be brought in, then they need to state that in the chart and refer the patient back to the PCP to make—or not make—that next referral. If the family is highly treatment-resistant and walks out on the PCP and her unwelcome behavioral recommendations, then the next specialist they see needs to make sure that there will be a new PCP acting as hub. Anything short of that is substandard care and can make the medical community part of the problem.

And we need to communicate effectively with schools. Notes to "excuse" are the antithesis of that.

CHAPTER 16

Woulda, Coulda, Shoulda

OUR LITTLE FRIEND ELEANOR PRESENTED TO MY OFFICE with a common emotion-driven complaint, and I had a pretty good success rate for helping kids like her get back to school. However, the situations that involved preexisting family dysfunction or troublesome personality traits tended to be a lot more challenging. I had some really tough cases in my outpatient practice where the illness was entrenched in family dysfunction. A discussion of coping skills and a measured plan to get back to school were just not going to be enough. A solid MedPsych toolbox at my disposal would have likely decreased the pushback from some of these families, helped them to accept emotional support, and allowed for a fuller, speedier recovery of function. It is in these more complex scenarios that the benefits of a solid MedPsych skill set most clearly declare themselves.

Mandy came into my pediatric office one morning with her mother. It was the first time I had met either of them. She was a fourteen-year-old ninth grader in a large local regional high school. The first things I noticed in the process of connecting with these two was that Mom did almost all the talking while Mandy sat quietly, like a trapped little bird perched on the exam table. Her smallness was an optical illusion. It took me a while to register that Mandy was actually quite tall. She sat hunched over on the table, hands clenched together on her lap. When she raised a hand up to her face to remove a strand of hair, I could see she was trembling. When I spoke to her directly, she turned to her mother to answer.

Mandy's mother more than filled in the communication gap. She was friendly in a loud way that made me want to take a step back. She explained to me that her daughter took a fall during a basketball game a few weeks back, and suffered a concussion.

"Oh no," I said, looking at Mandy. "I'm sorry to hear that. When did this happen?"

She glanced at Mom again to resume the talking. It turned out it was two weeks prior. She had been cleared of any observable trauma in the emergency room. The discharge diagnosis was "mild closed head trauma." She was advised to rest until she felt better. But she didn't feel better. In fact, she was getting worse. Now, two weeks later, the school was asking when she could come back, requiring a doctor's note if she needed to stay out longer.

I asked Mandy to describe the nature of the fall for me, and this was where she found her confidence. She described in detail the unfortunate footwork that sent her skidding, falling and hitting her head. She pointed to the area of the skull that got conked. She described persistent dizziness and confusion and her mother joined in to emphasize that Mandy was unable to do any schoolwork. Mandy wrapped it up with a sense of urgency, telling me that she had a headache almost all the time. The tale finished, Mandy abruptly stopped talking and folded back in on herself like a windup doll whose spring had wound down. Mom stated for the third or fourth time that the reason they were in my office that day was because Mandy needed a note to excuse her from school. It was significant to me that they were not asking about concussion treatment or what recovery might look like or if they should see a specialist. They just needed that note.

Concussion aside, there was a lot going on here and I knew I wasn't going to figure it all out this visit. I did some basic education about concussions and their variable course. I made some recommendations, like avoiding electronics and going out for a short walk now and then. I felt like a waiter reading off the specials of the day when you know the customer just wants a burger. Mom took the note I offered and the two of them hustled out the door, as if afraid I would change my mind. I was left feeling a little uncomfortable about Mandy's anxiety level, which seemed through the roof, and her eagerness, almost desperation, to be able to stay home.

To not go to school.

Like any pediatrician, I recognized the loss of function, even if I didn't use that term. However, I thought of Mandy's school avoidance not as a symptom but more as a diagnosis: school-related anxiety. And inevitably, swirling around that impression of school avoidance were wisps of suspicion for embellishment, manipulation, and deceit. All of this was complicated by the ever-present temptation of accommodation which, for doctors and principals everywhere, is the infamous school note. I gave her that note for two more weeks, with recommendations for gradually getting her back in shape for school.

They came back two weeks later for a follow-up. Mandy was just as nervous. Her mother was less gregarious, more guarded. They needed another note. She had not gone outside at all. She didn't feel well enough to go out. She had sat around all day watching TV or being on social media. She felt she could hardly get off the sofa. All in all, she was getting worse, not better.

I was as kind and gentle with Mandy as I knew how to be. Her exam remained unremarkable. I told her I was concerned that being out of school was making it harder for her to go back. I did not challenge her report of worsening symptoms—not because I understood they were real but because I understood that a challenge like that would overwhelm Mandy and anger her mother. In other words, I was being diplomatic. I did say that at this point that it would make sense for her to try and get back to school for at least a few hours a day, and rest in the school nurse's office if she needed to. I said I would speak to the nurse directly to arrange it.

Mandy looked horrified, and began to cry. Mom looked very worried.

"Doctor, she can hardly move. We can't send her back to school."

There was clearly a high level of emotion in the room, and an odd enmeshment between mother and child. I asked how Dad was doing with all this. Mandy shot a worried glance at her mother who answered with a dismissive wave of her hand. "He's clueless. He works all the time, never home."

I was fully aware, long before my MedPsych experience, that bringing up the topic of emotions and family relationships could get very tricky when dealing with puzzling medical symptoms. That would usually be interpreted by the patient and family as dismissive, or as it's otherwise known, "I think it's all in your head." It would sound like I didn't believe her, like I thought she was exaggerating or manipulating or downright lying.

And to be honest, I was starting to feel like she was exaggerating or manipulating or downright lying.

I believed this not because she was bad. She seemed like a pretty nice kid. I believed she was derailed by something she didn't know how to manage, and that she turned to these deceptive tactics as a conscious strategy to be able to stay home. To be safe. So I fell back on Pediatrics 101: *Stick to the medical evidence that this was a mild head injury. Do your best to get the kiddo back in school without getting bogged down in discussions about whether she's "really" having the symptoms she is reporting.* The psychoeducation I provided did *not* include a discussion of how the emotional brain was essentially "tricking" her body into actually experiencing these symptoms, because I didn't understand that myself. My messaging remained simple: "Worries can show up in a lot of different ways."

I acknowledged—diplomatically—that the clinical course of concussions was quite variable and hard to predict. I reassured them that the mechanism of injury and her subsequent evaluation in the ER were indicators for a good outcome. I told them that I believed she needed to gradually increase her activity level and function, including school attendance, while taking rests when they were needed. All good stuff. But incomplete in very important ways.

At this point I believed Mandy was suffering, to be sure. But I did not believe she was experiencing post-concussive pain and fatigue to the extent she was reporting. I was also frustrated that Mandy's mom seemed as desperate as Mandy was for her not to go to school. School avoidance had become the primary focus for both of them. Mom's approach to all this suggested to me that either Mandy had pulled the wool over her eyes, or that Mom didn't have the fortitude to get Mandy back to school.

A month later Mandy was still not in school, I was getting calls from the principal, and Mandy and her mom were sounding even more desperate to have her stay home. When I saw them again, they were both angry that I wouldn't write another excuse for school; that I didn't seem to "get it." I found myself trying to squish down my own defensive reaction to Mom's hostility.

What was I not able to tell Mandy at that visit? I could not tell her that I believed her head really did hurt and that she indeed felt as physically incapacitated as she said she did.

I certainly knew that concussions could potentially cause long-term severe symptoms and deficits. But given the relatively mild mechanism of injury and the fact that the focus was entirely on not going to school, I did not believe that Mandy was exhibiting chronic concussive symptoms. Hindsight would prove me right about that much. But that logically left me with the impression that she must then be consciously embellishing her symptoms, and that Mom was sheepishly falling for it. Hindsight was not as kind regarding that assessment.

I did not write another school note. I referred her to the concussion clinic run by Pediatric Neurology at Hasbro Children's. It was a very reasonable next step, but it also felt like a punt. I didn't know what else to do. Fortunately, Peds Neurology did know what to do. Coming to the same conclusion I did, they referred Mandy to a program I knew little about: Hasbro's MedPsych Partial program.

Going back in time, what would have been different if I had a Med-Psych skill set when I met Mandy? I did not lack an understanding of concussions and all the challenges associated with managing them. But being MedPsych-informed would have sharpened my clinical radar and diagnostic skills in addressing the emotional aspects of Mandy's symptoms. It would have put us all on a rockier but straighter path to meeting Mandy's needs.

Most importantly, I would have recognized the specific pattern of symptoms for what they were:

Loss of function: Mandy had a desperate need to not go back to school that crowded out the actual medical concern—concussion—which we would typically expect to be front and center.

Accommodation: Mom completely embraced Mandy's loss of function and could not bring herself to set limits on electronics or lack of physical activity. She certainly was not going to send Mandy back into school. Parental and school accommodation of these illnesses can be one of the most frustrating parts to managing emotionally based illness in kids. On the other hand, I'm the one who wrote the school note to excuse those absences.

Treatment resistance: In addition to not adhering to my initial recommendations, my subsequent advice for a gradual, gentle return to school pushed both Mom and daughter into extreme distress. Mandy's symptoms worsened. In their eyes it was becoming clear that I wasn't smart enough, kind enough, interested enough. For me it felt like I was up against a brick wall. I was relieved to be able to refer them to concussion experts.

Altered family dynamics: It was clear that Mom and Dad were not on the same page regarding Mandy's illness, and Mom was not interested in discussing his point of view. Her younger brother was filed under, "Does not need our attention right now." As I would someday learn, "not needing attention right now" is almost never the case for the siblings of MedPsych patients. In the family meetings of my future I would see just how much some of the siblings were suffering.

How would MedPsych training have changed the conversation?

I could have looked Mandy in the eye and told her honestly that I believed she was experiencing headache and dizziness. I would have been able to genuinely acknowledge her pain and suffering, rather than try to find the least offensive words to convey that I did not think her pain and dizziness were "physical." With MedPsych training I would have explained, with conviction, how the emotional brain was misfiring and sending her body the wrong messages. I would have acknowledged the anxiety level in the room, and validated that it was quite understandable given the scary and somewhat mysterious nature of Mandy's symptoms. And I would have expected and tolerated the distress that this conversation would cause.

Would they still have stomped out of the room? Almost certainly. But at least I would have drawn a roadmap for them, put a pin where we were, and offered to help plot the course to recovery in a way that made sense.

This is the need that the concussion specialists at Hasbro recognized, and that the MedPsych Partial program at Hasbro was able to address. I had heard of this partial (day) hospitalization program before, but had little sense of how it functioned. I would, a few years hence, come to learn that it was a pioneering program co-directed by a pediatrician and a psychiatrist. The program had a remarkable success rate and provided the blueprint for the Inpatient MedPsych unit I would someday call home.

Mandy and her parents had to agree to get Mandy to the program every day. Given the fact that the neurologists would not approve further school absenteeism, the family had little choice. The only other option was truancy or more doctor shopping. Both parents would be required to participate in the therapy, and Mandy's brother would be included at some point. On the other hand, the neurologists and Med-Psych doctors were able to reassure Mandy and her family that because of the groundbreaking integrated nature of the MedPsych program, she would be monitored medically as well as emotionally. Their medical concerns were not going to simply be dismissed.

Addressing function is almost always the first move. Having to get up and out the door every morning to attend the Partial program was in itself a giant therapeutic step forward for Mandy. The program included intensive psychiatric and psychological therapy for both Mandy and her family, group therapy with peers, and pediatric supervision that included monitoring her symptoms, coordination of nutritional and rehabilitative therapies, and of course ongoing collaboration with Pediatric Neurology.

Mandy did very well and was discharged from the MedPsych Partial program after four weeks. Dr. DerMarderosian, the medical director, called and spoke to one of my colleagues when Mandy was discharged, as I was not in the office that day. She went over Mandy's course, and alerted us to some of the family issues that emerged during her treatment there. Dr. DerMarderosian detailed all the steps they had taken to coordinate a smooth transition back to school for Mandy (she had successfully attended several days of school while in the Partial program), as well as the referrals and first appointments they made for outpatient individual and family counseling.

I didn't see Mandy again until almost a year later when she came in for a school physical. She was still quiet and soft-spoken, but was quite willing to see me privately for the first part of our visit, as was our typical practice with teens. She smiled often and answered questions directly. She told me she had switched to volleyball.

"No heading the ball," I said with mock sternness. She laughed a polite little laugh, the way teens do when a grownup thinks they're being funny.

"I promise I won't," she said, still smiling.

At that point I still had little idea of what went on in the MedPsych program, or why it was so successful. I was just really happy to see that it worked for Mandy.

CHAPTER 17

Down the Rabbit Hole

INTEGRATED CARE REFERS TO MUCH MORE THAT AN INTEGRA-
tion of specialties within the MedPsych program. It also reflects a
continuity of care between different levels of service. The MedPsych
day program was more formally known as Hasbro's Partial Hospitalization program and so was more commonly referred to as HPHP around
the hospital corridors. To us on the Inpatient MedPsych unit, however, it
was simply "Partial," like a family nickname that was whittled down out
of familiarity and relationship. In this family, the Partial program was
actually the "mom." The Inpatient MedPsych program up on Hasbro's
sixth floor had been the brainchild of the same folks who had developed
the HPHP. The more HPHP's reputation grew over the years, the more
they were receiving referrals for patients that were much too impaired
to be managed with a day program. The MedPsych program needed
an inpatient version of HPHP, and thus the Inpatient unit—the unit
where I would someday work—was born.

The criteria for needing HPHP care versus Inpatient MedPsych
care were varied and often nuanced. Safety was the most obvious line

in the sand. If a patient grew suicidal or was causing self-harm over the course of treatment in the Partial program, they were transferred up to us where we could provide 24-7 supervision as therapy proceeded. Most parameters were more subtle. If the patient or family's treatment resistance was escalating in response to HPHP therapies, or the patient was showing increasing physical symptoms that were sending them off to the emergency room after hours, we knew they might benefit from more intense monitoring and therapy on the Inpatient side for a while. If a patient was complying with the meal plan in the day program, but then escalating his food restriction and weight loss when he was with his parents in the evenings and on weekends, the family would be advised to come up to us to regroup. The patient's plan would remain the same. But the support would be 24-7. Such a move to Inpatient status, though often stormy, was usually also brief. This "vertical" integration in the intensity of care was as critical to treatment success for some patients as our integration of medical and psychiatric disciplines.

I had very limited experience with HPHP as a primary care provider out in the community. Mandy was one of a very few of my previous outpatients that had been treated there. That all began to change on my interview day, when I sat in Au Bon Pain with Diane DerMarderosian, the HPHP medical director, and Michelle Rickerby, the HPHP psychiatry director. I took an instant liking to them, and we all sat at our little table for far longer than the scheduled time slot. I answered all their questions and listened with fascination about the program that they were both so proud of. Diane, being a pediatrician like myself, fascinated me most of all. She was talking about the psychiatric implications of their patient population as fluently as she did the medical implications. She and Michelle had a rapport that struck me as a professional marriage, as if one could have completed the other's sentence. They were energetic and enthusiastic as they expounded on some of the program's more common diagnoses and how they were managed. My head was spinning with cases and diagnoses and medications and family therapy and fully integrated care. It was actually kind of thrilling. I really liked being a pediatrician, and felt privileged to be one, but it had been a long time since I had found any of it thrilling.

A few months after that interview I was showing up for my first day of work on the MedPsych unit, and Dan Spencer went over the day's schedule with me. One of the things he put on my list was "Up/Down" Meeting.

"What's that?" I asked.

It sounded like something out of *Alice in Wonderland*. Little did I know that I would soon be jumping down into that rabbit hole on a regular basis, and looking forward to it.

"Up/Down," it turned out, was our weekly meeting with the Partial staff. We met to discuss who from our unit might be ready to "step down" or transition to the Partial program, and who from the Partial program might need to "step up" to our higher level of care. But the term was as spatially pertinent as it was clinically. Our Inpatient unit was on the top floor of Hasbro Children's Hospital, and the Partial program was on the basement level of a much older building on the campus. We would get there by following a complicated system of underground corridors or "tunnels" as they were called, to the other side of the hospital campus. My first thought as we stepped into this world of laundry carts and worn-out linoleum was that I could never find my way back alone. I crashed into Dan more than once as we navigated the quick rights and lefts that would get us back to daylight.

I did eventually learn how to get to Partial all by myself, but I was glad I didn't often have to. That ten-minute power walk over to Partial with Dan gave us a unique weekly opportunity for conversation. We were free-range doctors for a sliver of time and we'd talk about clinical things, personal things, administrative things, without an agenda. I always had a lot of questions. But that first Monday, as we made our way back through the labyrinth after the meeting, the conversation felt more like a confession.

Sitting in my first Up/Down meeting my first day on the job I listened as Diane made references to all kinds of psychological parameters that indicated which unit, the Partial program or Inpatient service, was best suited for a particular patient. She felt that the current rate of weight gain for one of the Inpatients we mentioned was inadequate and that we needed to step up her nutrition a bit more. I didn't quite get it. It seemed to me they had as strong nutritional support in Partial as we did on the Inpatient unit. I was even more confused that Dan readily agreed with her.

I was further mystified with Diane's clinical assessment when she talked about a Partial parent's insistence that more medical tests be done. She felt that their continued resistance to therapy suggested the family needed our more intensive program upstairs. I could not have broken down a single one of her sentences into what was a medical and what was a psychiatric issue, and was feeling too overwhelmed in that moment to realize that that was the whole point.

An awful feeling came over me. If this was what fully integrated MedPsych treatment looked like from a pediatrician's view then I might be in over my head.

An hour later as Dan and I got buzzed out of the Partial unit and began to retrace our steps, he asked in his friendly, nonchalant way, "So what did you think?" I slowed, and then stopped in the empty corridor, and looked at him. I had to be honest. There was too much at stake.

"Dan, what Diane did back there—I can't do that. I don't think I understood the reasoning behind half of what she said."

He kind of chuckled and replied, "That's because it's your first day. Diane has been at this for years. And she is very, very good at what she does. You will be too."

I wasn't convinced. This job wasn't simply about applying my experience and knowledge to a different population of kids. It was going to require that I shift my way of thinking in some very fundamental ways. It would require that I measure illness and recovery by completely new parameters and actually integrate medical and psychiatric care in every clinical judgment I made. This concept of integrated care was not about different disciplines playing nice together. It was about seamless collaboration. The right hand knowing to expect what the left hand needed to do, and understanding why. I realized that what I had been hearing in Au Bon Pain from Diane and Michelle was not just collegiality. It was living, breathing, integrated care.

I managed to shake off my first day jitters and very quickly realized that Diane was my greatest ally. She checked in with me frequently, was always positive and supportive, and most of all, she taught me. Her guidance was gentle. As I was getting ready to discharge a patient she'd call me to congratulate me on the therapeutic success, and then she would often add a casual question.

"Were the physical therapists able to come up with a transition plan with a therapist near her home?"

Hmmm. PT. Did I not think to tell the physical therapists that that the patient was discharging? I was pretty sure that was what Diane's question was really aimed at. Of course PT would want to ensure an outpatient plan was in place. But Diane was as good at teaching as she was at doctoring, and always left me room to come to the right conclusion myself. Thanks to Diane's support and kindness, most of the folks on the MedPsych team had little idea of how much guidance I was requiring in those early days. I was learning that once you fully understood integrated care you could apply it generously in many directions—Med and Psych, Up and Down, and even laterally, to a colleague who was getting her feet wet. Integration became not only a treatment approach, but the way to function overall.

The more time I spent in an integrated MedPsych program, where information between medical and behavioral providers flowed continuously, the more I realized how barriers to communication between these specialties in the outpatient setting stunted pediatric providers' professional growth. Psychiatrists and psychologists have to take patient confidentiality very seriously, and send little information about the clinical encounter or their thought processes back to the referring pediatrician. Contrast this to, say, a Pedi GI referral. It would usually be apparent from the referring doctor's report what the specialist's impressions were, the reasoning behind what should get ruled out, the lab tests they ordered to do it, why the patient would or would not need a medication, and what followup was needed. In other words, good consult reports provide the PCP with an ongoing flow of educational and clinical updates.

In RI we have a program that helps overcome some of these barriers with mental health treatment. It is called PediPRN and provides same-day telecommunication with a psychiatrist to pediatricians who feel they need guidance on management of a behavioral health issue. As pediatric mental health rapidly evolves into a common primary care issue, we need more of these innovative ways to integrate these two specialties.

CHAPTER 18

Getting Back on the Horse

INDIVIDUAL AND FAMILY TALK THERAPY WERE KEY ELEMENTS OF the MedPsych program, but restoring physical function in parallel to this was critical. Patients with functional loss from emotionally driven illness cannot think and talk their way back into their lives. If they could, they wouldn't need us to begin with. MedPsych treatment demonstrates that restoring normal function—whether it be a case of mobility loss, a pain syndrome, or nonepileptic convulsions—is a key element in resetting the emotional brain's control over the rest of the body. For Eleanor and Mandy, restoring function meant gently and compassionately supporting them to get back into school. For Mike, it meant ignoring his convulsions, no matter how dramatic, so that they no longer provided a barrier to him meeting the normal expectations for an adolescent. For Carla it meant incentivizing her to eat food by mouth again, even if the face of abdominal pain. Once the symptoms of emotionally based illness no longer provide protection from age-appropriate expectations, like school attendance or healthy eating habits, those symptoms are vanquished.

The psychiatric and pediatric assessments that led to these plans for functional recovery were crucial, but the providers who carried out the actual work, seeming to carry miracles around in their pockets, were the rehabilitation therapists and dieticians. I could picture my role in all this as a diner who knows nothing about French cooking. I can order from the menu, but can take no credit for the chateaubriand that ultimately appears in front of me. On MedPsych I could only take credit for knowing what the functional goals were for a patient and who could make it happen.

Who are the master chefs of MedPsych? The physical therapists, the occupational therapists, the speech and language therapists, and the dieticians. The Pain team were also standing by with a wide array of integrative modalities like massage and visual imagery. The work of all these folks was also a window into how emotionally based illness functions. All their treatments required that the patient, who had spent way too much time drowning in the passivity of the illness, now be an active participant in recovery.

Chelsea, a sixteen-year-old from Kansas, was a shining example of how these supporting specialists took my assessment and ran with it. Chelsea had sustained a nonspecific knee injury while ice skating over a year prior to admission. The pain and debilitation it caused only grew worse over time, without any objective findings or medical explanation. By the time she arrived on our unit Chelsea was in a wheelchair and had gained fifty pounds. She winced with the slightest movement, but kept up a brave smile as she and her mom told us their story.

Chelsea had not attended school for months. She had seen many specialists, and had multiple courses of outpatient physical therapy. Each time, she would work hard and make good progress. But as soon as she was cleared to go back to school she would have a relapse that brought worse pain and more limited function. She had agreed to emotional therapy but it was going nowhere. By the time her pediatrician contacted us Chelsea was unable to maneuver out of her house due to worsening leg and now back pain. She needed assistance to use the bathroom and needed adaptive equipment to shower.

Chelsea would eagerly agree to try emotional work but predicted, correctly, that it would accomplish nothing, and back under her blankets she would go. Her mother was heartbroken at how diminished her daughter's life had become and felt guilty and completely powerless to help her. Chelsea's mother in fact had been sick herself, with chronic fatigue. Chelsea's father had left them just shortly after Chelsea's birth and she had had no contact with him.

Chelsea was a sweet, friendly girl and, in a departure from the usual reaction teens had to being admitted to MedPsych, she put a lot of effort her first few days into letting us know she was on our team and would do anything we asked—even though, she'd point out with good-natured realism, it probably wasn't going to work. Although I was surprised to hear her willingness to work with us, given the lack of progress she'd shown up to that point, I was also a bit relieved. It would be a nice change to simply help someone who was so eager to get better. We wouldn't have to go through that exhausting "treatment resistance" stage.

Coming up against treatment resistance, which up to that point I had seen as a constant feature of MedPsych illness, felt to me at times like I was stepping out of the research base at the South Pole and into the raw blizzard of Antarctica. No amount of thermal protection was going to make the outing pleasant. Of course the psychologists, remarkable species that they are, would see this harsh landscape of distress as pure opportunity. Distress was the key that opened the door to recovery. No matter how much I wanted to stay in the warm base station, the therapists couldn't wait to jump out into the storm. While I, as a pediatrician, had always seen human distress as something that needed to be alleviated, the psychiatrists and psychologists saw it as an invitation. It was the whole reason they had come to Antarctica in the first place.

My initial relief at Chelsea's great attitude was short-lived. As the team sat in rounds that first morning, I presented her medical history and current findings, and threw in the good news about her highly cooperative mindset.

"Yeah, we've got our work cut out for us here," said Dr. Hagin. "This one's gonna be tough."

Wait. What?

Jesse was the lead physical therapist and the point person for coordinating all the different kinds of rehab a patient might need. My consultant request to her was the medical version of "I'll have the chateaubriand." It would have read something like this:

"Sixteen-year-old girl with chronic, worsening unexplained knee pain that has severely limited her mobility, school attendance, and activities of daily living. Please assess and advise as to plan for restoring this patient's function."

In short: "This girl has emotionally driven illness. Please help."

And Jesse would bring the chateaubriand.

Jesse would know exactly what to do. She and her rehab colleagues would connect with Chelsea, bringing warmth and optimism that cannot be taught. They would educate her on the mechanical aspects of their therapies. They would validate her pain and at the same time start talking about what her knee was safely able to do. They would suggest a gradual strengthening program that would start with bearing a little bit of weight on her toes while leaning on a therapist. Each day they would do a little more. Meanwhile, occupational therapy would come up and assist with her shower every day and if needed, the physical therapist would join them. They would gradually minimize the supportive devices she would have in the shower with her, and suggest tiny increments of more independent self-care.

Over the following weeks, Chelsea worked hard in PT, only to crawl back in bed afterwards, asking for dinner to be brought to her. The session, she lamented, had only made her pain more excruciating. Chelsea's physical therapists, however, were stronger than Chelsea's symptoms. They just kept showing up, meeting her where she was, never challenging her reports of pain which they accepted as real, but gently coaxing her to move through it to the best of her ability. With the help of Dr. Hagin, who was providing intense individual and family support, they found an open door: Chelsea loved riding horses and line dancing, things her illness had forced her to give up. So her PT sessions started to include gentle dance steps to the sound of country music. Before long they brought in stairs and other props to mimic the moves Chelsea would need in order to get on a horse. Meanwhile the Palliative Care team reviewed and streamlined her pain meds, offered yoga and massage, and helped her identify useful coping skills. Success bred success.

The physical, occupational, and speech and language therapists achieved these kinds of remarkable outcomes in countless MedPsych patients. I met with them on a weekly basis to review the patients' progress and update them on any new behavioral or medical issues that may have come up. In turn, they taught me so much. I was astounded by their expertise and all the creative ways they could apply their knowledge.

The same was true for Dr. Angie Anderson and her Palliative Care team. When Angie met with me to discuss a patient and her reasoning as to why one med should be tapered or another med introduced, I would actually take notes. My brain would feel like it was swelling with all the education she could provide in a fifteen-minute conversation— even as I kept erupting into laughter at her very quirky humor. I pointed out many times to Angie and Jesse and their fellow team members, and to my MedPsych colleagues as well, that these professionals made our whole team look good and that our program and patients could never attain the success they did without the ongoing guidance and dedication of these rehabilitative and pain specialists. I would think of this every time someone patted me on the back for doing a great job with a patient, or a parent thanked me with tears in their eyes. I thought about how many times Lydia must have cursed at her occupational therapist, or Alyssa screamed at the speech therapist to get out of her room. Effective MedPsych treatment relied not only on integrating pediatric and psychiatric practice, but on a whole network of healthcare providers beyond our team who were committed to the slow, uphill, labor-intensive teamwork of the MedPsych program.

Throughout Chelsea's hospitalization, I continued in my usual role. That meant evaluating ongoing or new pain, taking her symptoms seriously, consulting with her team, clearing her to continue physical and occupational therapy, and cheering her on. A month later she walked out of the unit and over to the Partial program in cowboy boots, flanked by Jesse on one side of her and her proud mother on the other.

Most patients transitioned to our Partial program before being discharged to home and outpatient care. Chelsea, like most of our inpatients, had made excellent progress in our intense, round-the-clock program, where parents were part of the decision-making progress but had limited hours for visiting their teen on the unit. The Partial program was an intermediate step in handing the control back over to the parents. It was not unusual that once the Partial day ended and the child got back home—or the Ronald McDonald House or a hotel for those who were far from home—the patient would regress, symptoms would flare, parents would panic. The Partial program provided the same type of intensive therapies that the Inpatient program did, while gradually pulling away from the intensity of twenty-four-hour support. Sure enough, Chelsea regressed as soon as the structure lessened, and refused to go back to Partial the second day because she was having so much leg pain from the increased walking she had been doing.

This resistance was the "pure gold" that Fran Pingatore, our psychoanalytic consultant, had taught me to recognize. The Partial program, and its expectations for a higher level of independent functioning, was flushing out any lingering residue of Chelsea's illness. The Partial folks knew exactly how to pull her through it. We would get weekly updates from our counterparts in the Partial program about how Chelsea and her mom were doing, and a month after Chelsea was discharged from Partial we heard that she was back in school in Kansas and riding her horse almost daily. Both her and her mom were continuing therapy as outpatients.

Use of rehabilitative therapists is often an essential part of MedPSych treatment, especially for symptoms like headache, dizziness and weakness. But it is one that is often underutilized in the outpatient world. This is likely related to a combination of factors including insurance issues and access to pediatric rehab providers. The more we can address these barriers, the more success we will enjoy with our more challenging outpatient kiddos.

CHAPTER 19

Cecily's Pain

I AM GRATIFIED THAT IN MY PREVIOUS OUTPATIENT PRAC-
tice I was able to get most of the kiddos with emotionally based illness back on track, even if I stumbled here and there when the going
got rough. I also remember all too well that there were families I could
just not reach. These are the ones I would think about as I watched a kid
like Chelsea reclaim her life. I will always wonder what would have happened if I had only been a little smarter about emotionally based illness
in some of my tougher outpatient encounters.

Cecily had been in my practice since infancy. Her medical history
was unremarkable except that as a preschooler she had severe constipation, and began to gain too much weight. When she was four years old
she developed encopresis—a miserable result of severe constipation that
causes liquid stool to leak out involuntarily, a little at a time, throughout
the day. This is the result of chronic obstruction from constipation, and
is a social nightmare for the child. The treatment is a good old-fash-
ioned cleanout with enemas or rectal suppositories and laxatives, which

is also not a great experience for a child. The follow-up includes lots of liquids and high fiber foods as well as a regimented plan for toileting.

Doctors have known for a long time now that constipation has an increased rate of occurrence in children who are anxious or depressed. With preschoolers it's hard to know what comes first, the constipation or the emotional flare.

Childhood constipation is an extremely common issue in primary pediatric care. Every pediatrician I knew had premade handouts to give parents on what causes constipation, what treatments to use and how to use them, and what kind of toileting regimen should be instituted once the major blockage is cleared. In young children who seemed to live in a safe, stable home, the standard treatment plan was usually effective. If things didn't go well, and especially if there was encopresis, then we would have to address any underlying anxieties more directly, as well as the terrible toll this illness takes on self-esteem.

Still, it was all in a day's work. Constipation was a common issue and one of those issues that brought physical, social, and emotional challenges all together at once. Most of the time our interventions moved the child along. But not always. Not with Cecily.

Cecily had just started kindergarten, and around that time she began to complain again about frequent abdominal pain. Importantly, she had not had a recurrence of bowel leakage. Her physical exam that day suggested constipation based on the rock formations I could palpate in her belly. An X-ray confirmed it. But there was more. Cecily sat very quietly on the exam table, looking like she might start crying any minute. She was a sad, overweight little girl who looked terrified of me despite our history and my quiet, careful approach. I was also struck by Mom. She had always been a bit anxious herself, but generally appreciative of the time I would take to answer her many questions. But this visit was different. Mom had a battle to fight, and she was geared up.

"Dr. Kozel, we've recently discovered that all this time you've been treating Cecily for constipation she's actually had celiac disease."

A quick shot of defensiveness flared up inside of me. I hadn't expected this. Confusion added to the mix as I learned from Mom that she had brought Cecily to a holistic doctor on the recommendation of a friend. All Cecily's tests were negative, as were Mom's and Dad's, and there was no family history of celiac or other chronic gastrointestinal disease, but the doctor she brought Cecily to insisted that this was all gluten sensitivity—something that "most doctors don't understand." Then, in a voice that sprayed frustration at me Mom added, "So I had to find this all out for myself." She was angry. Her anger made me nervous and defensive.

Regrouping, I fell back on my old standard approach: information. I talked about what celiac disease was and how it was diagnosed. I talked about all the other ways celiac disease can show up in the body, and that thankfully Cecily had none. I'm pretty sure my cheeks were red the entire discussion even though my voice was steady. Cecily's mom just shook her head at me and my ignorance. Then came the final revelation:

"Cecily hasn't been able to go to school for weeks now because of the belly pain."

"You said she has been off gluten for over a month," I responded, ever the logical doctor. "But I'm hearing that her symptoms are only getting worse, and now she can't even get to school."

"Well that's why I am so frustrated, Doctor. Clearly her bowels have been through a lot. If we had discovered this sooner, she probably wouldn't be constipated now."

I stood there blinking at her emotional response, still operating on the mindset that I could clear this all up with a bit of parent education. But Cecily's mom had already written me off.

I may not have recognized all the patterns of emotionally based illness that were swirling around that room at the time, but school absenteeism in an anxious girl with abdominal pain and no medical evidence of gastrointestinal pathology is a call to action for a pediatrician. I was going to have to somehow quell my defensiveness to Mom's hostility, button up all my unwelcome diagnostic opinions, and convince angry Mom that the top priority was to get Cecily back in her classroom. I recommended a pediatric gastroenterology consult, laid out a recommended treatment for the constipation, and advised sending Cecily to school for a few hours a day. I told Mom that with her permission I could call the principal to explain our plan. Cecily started to cry. Mom picked Cecily up and headed for the door, without a word.

I stood there in the office for a moment to collect myself. I was stunned and confused by Mom's unwillingness to have a rational discussion about celiac disease. And, I'll admit it, I was hurt and angry myself. I had cared for Cecily since she was a baby.

Somebody call a MedPsych-informed doctor! Stat!

If only I could have called upon Diane DerMarderosian about the best way to approach Mom's focus on celiac disease, or Sarah Hagin about the treatment resistance, or Dan Spencer about the family enmeshment. If only Michelle Rickerby could remind me that distress can be a roadmap. If only I had Fran Pingatore waiting out there in the hall to explain transference and countertransference—again—so that I'd learn to manage my reactions to unexpected anger and hostility. If only.

What would I have done differently with a MedPsych skill set? The simple ability to recognize and frame the features of Cecily's emotionally driven symptoms would have allowed me to take a giant step back. It would have been my guide to a more effective approach.

First, I would have acknowledged to Cecily and her mom that Cecily seemed to be experiencing a lot of belly pain, even when she wasn't constipated and was avoiding gluten, and that must feel terrible. And scary. I would say this with complete honesty because I would believe that Cecily *was* really experiencing pain. I would have understood that this is the work of the emotional brain, deflecting anxiety signals into real bodily symptoms.

I would definitely not have gotten into a debate about diagnoses. I would have confidence in knowing that unhelpful diagnoses would fall by the wayside as the emotional issues were addressed. Instead I would have offered practical advice:

"Let's at least treat the constipation and see if that reduces the pain at all."

I would have tried pulling Cecily into the conversation a bit more instead of defending myself from Mom's distress. I might ask Cecily if she missed school (100 percent likelihood that she would have said yes and her mom would have chimed in about how she was a great student, her teachers loved her, etc.). I would have asked what Cecily missed most about school, and align with her about how hard missing that thing— her teacher, recess, the hamster, whatever—must be. I would ask Cecily if anything about school scared her, and gotten specific about toileting issues, but would also not be dissuaded if she denied any anxiety at all about anything. I would acknowledge to Mom, genuinely, how worried she and Dad must be, without challenging their working diagnosis. I would have found the space to ask Mom a little bit about where Dad stood in all of this. Even if Mom was convinced of my incompetence, she would see that I wasn't doubting their story, or thinking Cecily was faking. She might have moved a few inches into alignment with me.

And I could have provided more psychoeducation. I would delicately approach the subject of feelings and how the emotional part of our brains can misfire when we get worried, and make our physical symptoms more intense.

I might still have had a kneejerk response to Mom's hostility but I also would have immediately recognized the parent's behavior for what it was: an overpowering urge to prevent the child's distress by accommodating the symptoms that kept Cecily out of school. Recognizing this and accepting it as part of the symptom complex rather than a personal attack on me would have almost certainly made for a better interaction.

Getting a second opinion from an actual pediatric gastroenterologist made sense, given how focused the family seemed to be on the information they were getting from the other doctor and their conviction that gluten was the reason for the school absenteeism. If Mom's anger had subsided a bit she probably would have agreed to that.

And then I would have to poke the emotional bear waiting in the corner of the room. I would recommend that after completing a bowel cleanout, Cecily needed to start easing her way back into school, and I would make sure it was done in a planful way.

There's a fair chance this would have worked and we could have gotten down to the business of restoring Cecily's function; i.e. returning to school. If instead this remained too overwhelming a prospect for mother and/or child, they might have aligned with me enough to agree to therapy.

Or they may still have stormed out of the room, frustrated, frightened, and mad. But my chances of the more positive outcome would have been so much greater if my approach had been more informed. Even if they had still rejected my advice, I would likely have planted a seed that the pediatric gastroenterologists at Hasbro could cultivate. They may have even been successful in referring them to the MedPsych Partial program, as the pediatric neurologists did for Mandy. Unlike our adolescent-focused Inpatient program, Partial had a program not only for adolescents but for younger children as well, and Cecily would have been a great referral. Like Peds Neurology, Peds Gastro developed a strong relationship with the Partial program, and having a MedPsych-informed recommendation from me would have better aligned us all with getting Cecily the right care.

What actually happened was that Cecily's family left the practice, feeling more comfortable with a "doctor who understood celiac disease." It's painful to look back and think about how I might have shaped a better outcome if I could have tapped into a MedPsych mindset. Even if that didn't work, at least I would have understood why. I would not have walked around the rest of that day after Cecily's visit wearing a crown of thorns. And that would have been a very healthy outcome in itself.

CHAPTER 20

And on That Note

THE STORIES OF EMOTIONALLY BASED ILLNESS IN THIS BOOK underscore a critical element of these disorders: accommodation. Whether we are talking about a teenage boy admitted for nonepileptic seizures or an endearing little cherub in my office whose tummy aches kept her from school, we know that these situations cannot exist without the grownups in their lives smoothing the path for them. It's true for little Cecily, whose parents took off time from work in order to get doctor's notes to excuse any absences. It's true for her teachers, who send work home along with cheery notes.

It's true for her pediatrician who is caught in a very awkward situation. If the doctor refuses to write a medical excuse the parents will be furious and the school will be confused. Principals will call the office to plead the child's case. They are all good people and they are all emotionally involved. Meanwhile the pediatrician can share very little about what she thinks is actually going on unless the parents consent to that—which they usually don't.

I tried to find a middle road with Cecily and avoid excusing her absence with a lukewarm "I saw Cecily in my office today for complaints of abdominal pain. Her exam was unremarkable and she needs no further interventions at this time. She may return to school." Unfortunately even that would likely earn the child an excused absence. Reading between the lines works both ways.

The first rule of MedPsych treatment is to not accommodate symptoms. So Mike, the kiddo with nonepileptic seizures, will not get special padding or rails on his bed on our unit. If he has a convulsive episode, the staff ignores it. If he slides from his chair in the middle of group therapy and begins to flail and writhe on the floor, the therapist will calmly lead the rest of the group out of the room to another quiet spot, with a side comment to the nurse to keep an eye on him. We know that kids with nonepileptic convulsions are very unlikely to injure themselves during these episodes. And as day follows the night, when the seizures no longer prompt others into treating the child as if he or she needs special assistance or accommodations, the episodes become less frequent. Mike's emotions lost their dysfunctional escape route as soon as he stepped through those MedPsych doors. When this is combined with good therapeutic support, suppressed emotions rise to the surface, exposed.

This understanding of the role of accommodation in fueling MedPsych symptoms brought me back to Eleanor and Cecily and all the other kiddos with school avoidance that I encountered.

In the years leading up to my position on MedPsych I served as the "school physician" for a large school district in Rhode Island. In that role I tried to convince the school superintendent to do away with "excused" vs "non-excused" absences, arguing that not only did this reinforce school avoidance and other anxiety conditions, but also was based on a misguided notion that absenteeism due to a "real illness" puts a child in less jeopardy than missing school because she keeps oversleeping. That is simply not true. When kids are frequently missing school due to emotionally driven symptoms then they are shielding themselves from appropriate developmental tasks that await in the academic, social, and emotional aspects of school. This loss is as grave to them as to a kiddo who can't get out of bed in the morning. They (and their families) need support, not accommodation. Excused absences only invite the principal, the teachers, and the doctor into the dysfunctional dynamic of emotionally driven illness.

MedPsych illnesses are real illnesses with real symptoms that deserve our attention. But giving Eleanor a green light to stay home makes no more sense than writing a doctor's note that says Suzie, who has diabetes, shouldn't go to school if her morning blood sugar is over 150. Nobody would ever say that. Suzie would have a diabetes management plan at home and on file in the nurse's office at school that would cover this very situation. And if Suzie keeps showing up at school with blood sugars over 150, the question is "What needs to change?" not "Can I get a doctor's excuse to keep her home?" The same is true of emotionally based illness. Giving a note to excuse Cecily from school makes no more sense than telling Suzie to stay home because she has diabetes. Cecily and her parents need emotional support and guidance. And Cecily needs to get back to school. Whether the issue at hand is diabetes or school-related anxiety, communication between the pediatrician and the school is critical. A doctor's note of excuse is nothing more than an inappropriate accommodation of an illness that thrives on exactly that.

Doctor's notes also open the door to all kinds of social disparities. I can guarantee that if my daughter was missing school due to frequent tummy aches, her kind, wonderful teachers in my close-knit community would have bent over backwards to reassure and accommodate her. There are those "errors of kindness" again. In a struggling community like South Providence, however, outpatient doctor visits can feel like a luxury barely within grasp, and a school note requires bus fare, an appointment with a physician you may have never met before, and possibly lost time at work that the parent cannot afford. So there likely won't be a note. Chronic absenteeism in these situations is unlikely to be addressed until it meets the criteria for truancy. The teachers in South Providence are as kind and wonderful as the teachers in my town. It's just a different ecosystem which by its very nature leans less on accommodation and more on enforcement.

Do doctors need to communicate with schools if their patient has a medical condition that is impacting participation in school? Absolutely. All the school nurses and teachers I have ever spoken with on the subject have been eager for information and eager to help. Unfortunately, unlike parents of diabetics, parents of children with school-related anxieties are often hesitant to allow such communication. They are afraid the child will be stigmatized, or the teachers may not be as patient and understanding as we would hope. This is what needs to change. If all parties can all start from the premise that the child is experiencing actual physical symptoms, that they are not consciously being manipulative, and that this is a highly treatable condition, then we are poised for success. We can align with parents by ensuring we will continue medical monitoring while a behavior plan or counseling is put in place. We are not dismissing them or the symptoms. And we know how to help the child get back on track.

For many of us this will require some shift in mindset. For a few of us, who still hearken back to the days when "you went to school unless you were bleeding," it may require a larger shift. But it needs to happen. Medical accommodation of emotionally driven illness is substandard care, and doctor's notes are their oxygen. Doctor's notes need to go the way of the dinosaur. More open, productive channels of communication between pediatricians and schools are what all children deserve.

CHAPTER 21

Linguistic Minefields

ONE OF THE CHILD PSYCHIATRISTS ON THE UNIT, DR. Mirabelle Mattar, would often comment on the inadequacy of MedPsych language. The most glaring example, as she would point out, was the term "MedPsych" itself. As we all know, psychiatry is a branch of medicine. Integrating "psych" with "med" is like saying you are going to combine peanut butter and food to make a sandwich. But this is the language we are stuck with. The issue takes on greater significance, however, when we realize how vocabulary shapes mindsets and how mindsets shape vocabulary. The chicken and the egg. It's a hard cycle to break.

The irony of course is that probably no other medical specialty spills over into all the other specialties the way psychiatry does, and yet it remains in many of our minds and our speech as something apart from medicine. Neurologists are certified by the American Board of Psychiatry and Neurology. When I asked my husband, a neurologist, why the certification is from a joint board he shrugged as if it was the most common union in the world and answered "It's all brain stuff." The most important truths are often the simplest ones.

Pediatric gastroenterologists have as much appreciation of the psychiatric influences on our health as neurologists do. They refer to the gut as the "second brain" due to the fact that the gastrointestinal tract contains a complex system of neurons and neurotransmitters similar to those that define the "first" brain—the one that sits just north of our ear canals. Most of us take for granted that there is an association between mood issues and GI symptoms. It's why nervous first graders throw up on the school bus and a big interview might send us running to the nearest public restroom. Pediatric gastroenterologists deal with these connections every day. Irritable bowel syndrome for example is famous for blurring the lines between emotions and intestinal function. And it's a two-way street. Ulcerative colitis is associated with anxiety and depression, and emotional distress in turn causes flares of ulcerative colitis. More chickens and eggs. Dr. Mattar's point is well taken. Every time we utter "MedPsych" we foster the very misconceptions about our health we are trying to help patients overcome.

The term MedPsych is not the only linguistic pretzel we have to contend with. Even the term *mind-body connection* can, in this setting, suggest an unhelpful duality that undermines the unifying concept of emotionally driven illness. The mind is basically a function of the brain. You can't have a mind without a brain that produces it. If you take two baby steps past that definition the conversation can quickly drift into the metaphysical. That's just not helpful in the setting of MedPsych treatment. Parents don't want interesting conversation. They want answers. So we stress the simple fact that the brain is most definitely a part of the body, and the brain's functioning is a part of the body's overall functioning. When you take a math test—the one that's making your bowels gurgle unpleasantly by the way—your brain is getting its calculating energy from the glucose that your intestines absorbed at breakfast and that your pancreas is now regulating. It is getting its oxygen from the blood that your heart sends pulsing through it.

If we are used to thinking that the mind is *connected* to the body rather than being *a function* of it, then we already have a bias in our thinking that makes understanding MedPsych illness difficult. We don't describe the heart as something that is connected to the body. When a problem with the heart causes kidney damage, we are not the least bit confused as to how that could possibly happen. Similarly MedPsych treatment teaches us that Mike's emotional brain—which is also part of Mike's body—can express itself through the *rest* of his body by triggering his arms to flail about in bizarre but totally harmless ways. It's all real. It's all medical. It's just not epilepsy. It's driven by highly organized signals from the emotional brain and we see the results manifest themselves in other parts of the body.

But we are not used to thinking or talking about psychiatric illness in that medical way. This is the linguistic minefield I needed to cross in a family meeting when all the eyeballs in the room are focused on me. I can offer all the support and reassurance I want—"We know he's *not faking*. It is his *illness* that is causing him to experience these symptoms"—but once we get down into the weeds, and especially when we're trying to address the family's direct, logical questions, each of us, especially the not-so-therapeutically-trained pediatrician, have to constantly watch where we step.

Here's what the parents ask: "Doctor, we understand the EEGs (the test for seizures or epileptic activity), were normal, but clearly there is *something wrong*. We know our son. He loves school. He has great friends. He is not doing this for attention or whatever else people are thinking. And when Dr. So-and-so started him on Gabapentin, he actually seemed to show some improvement for a little while. So there's *obviously* something *medically* wrong."

This is where Dr. Mattar's point is so important. It's almost impossible to answer these very legitimate questions without saying things like there is no "medical" explanation for the seizures, even as we try to cultivate an understanding that psychiatry *is* medical. My answers to the parents' questions will rely on terms like the "emotional brain" as the source of the illness, and neuronal misfiring as the way it is transmitted. But beyond sophisticated, indirect imaging studies, none of us have actually observed that process. I will talk to the family about what Mike is *experiencing*—which is very real—rather than suggesting it is not "real" epilepsy, and hope that they will all follow me down that bumpy linguistic road.

Therapeutic MedPsych language demands that we—pediatricians as well as therapists—do our very best to emphasize how truly integrated these domains of brain function and observable bodily functions are. We all kind of get it already. We get that stress can cause ulcers, depression can cause headaches, sadness can cause tears. We accept these relationships because they are commonly experienced and somewhat traceable in terms of physiology. The notion of the emotional brain driving paralysis or joint pain or Mike's convulsions, however, is much fuzzier. This in turn means our word choices get fuzzier. For now.

Someday we will understand how brain signals coalesce into what we now call "thoughts" and "feelings." Someday we may identify "nanobubbles of intuition" (I totally made that up) that transport signals from the unconscious to the conscious brain. We might even understand the neurophysiologic basis for me thinking the term "nanobubbles of intuition" is amusing. But for now we are still channeling Aristotle and his humors. We conceptualize MedPsych illnesses as having tangible (neuroanatomic) and intangible (emotional) components that can affect both our behaviors and bodily functions. We know this even though we don't fully know how they connect to each other. We know this the way Aristotle knew that dietary changes and a walk in the fresh air goes a long way in curing gout: Because they do.

———— CHAPTER 22 ————

Illness Identity

ILLNESS IDENTITY IS A TERM THAT HAS BEEN USED IN PSYCHIA-try to describe the negative self-image a person may develop as a result of having been given a psychiatric diagnosis. For instance a person diagnosed with manic-depressive disorder may believe that this means they will never be able to have a "normal" life.

When we talk about MedPsych illness, the story gets more complex because the illness identity is based not on the acceptance of a psychiatric diagnosis but rather the rejection of it, and a tenacious belief that one's symptoms (or in the case of pediatric patients, one's child's symptoms) are entirely due to a medical condition, albeit one that defies medical explanation. In this sense of the term illness identity is not the unhappy reaction to hearing a worrisome psychiatric diagnosis. It is quite the opposite—an insistence that a debilitating illness is the result of a medical diagnosis, despite all evidence to the contrary.

My illness cannot be based in my emotional brain. Look at how sick I am. I can't walk. It must be a connective tissue disorder.

I am too weak to get out of bed. It must be a metabolic disorder.

I keep having convulsions. It must be a neurologic disorder.

Imagine the degree of control the emotional brain is exerting to keep an intelligent, previously active adolescent lying in his darkened bedroom, unable to meet the most basic expectations of adolescent life. He cannot consider the possibility that he could have a reasonably functional life—go to school, have dinner with his family, drive a car, meet up with friends. For whatever reasons, the normal life transitions he was facing triggered intolerable anxiety. His emotional brain jumped into self-preservation mode, sending signals to the body that it was too physically ill to meet the developmental expectations for his age. The physical symptoms offer emotional sanctuary. But it comes at a high cost. These symptoms are his exile as well.

Illness identity is a key component of this self-sabotage. The patient's symptoms are real, and any challenge to the medical diagnoses that are accumulating will be met with strong and often hostile resistance, just as they were for Cecily. In some cases, as the family looks for validation of the child's incapacitation, their efforts even can veer towards a distorted sort of self-promotion.

I remember one fourteen-year-old girl, Dani, from Florida who was wheelchair-bound as a result of her (undiagnosed) somatic symptom disorder, with her and her family frustrated and frightened that "the doctors have no idea what is making her so ill." They searched up and down the Eastern Seaboard for answers, finally getting a very definitive and very misguided diagnosis from a doctor in Maryland who championed Ehlers-Danlos syndrome like it was a religion. She based Dani's diagnosis on an exam she did in a hotel room in NYC. They were all in New York for an Ehlers-Danlos convention, and for a hefty fee you could get this speaker to come to your hotel room and do an evaluation of your child. On my preadmission review, I attempted to contact this doctor for more information, but she refused to return my calls. Still, she had already conveyed such certainty about the Ehlers-Danlos diagnosis to the family that they were convinced they finally had an answer.

Nobody wants that diagnosis for a family member, but such is the power of severe MedPsych illness. It is imperative to maintain a medical etiology. Once they had a diagnosis, Dani's family then brought her to Boston Children's to see one of the leading experts in the country on Ehlers-Danlos so that they could learn more and optimize her care. They went home crestfallen however, and quite angry, when the specialist told them she did not believe Dani had Ehlers-Danlos syndrome, and referred her to our program instead. This put the family in a bind. Their insurance company was not going to keep paying for care unless the family agreed to the Boston doctor's recommendation. Dani and her family came to us under a cloud of resentment.

After reviewing the records that came with Dani's referral, I called the Boston rheumatologist to get a better sense of how open this family might be to our program. One thing she said stuck in my head. She told me that the kids she sees with Ehlers-Danlos almost never show up in wheelchairs. They are running up and down the hall, beg to be allowed to play sports, and usually miss a minimum of school due to their symptoms despite the fact that they are in pain. It was heartbreaking, she said, because kids with Ehlers-Danlos really do have to restrict their physical activities. Paradoxically, in her experience, when a patient showed up in a wheelchair, and felt unable to attend school, they were the ones most likely to not have Ehlers Danlos, but rather a MedPsych illness. This observation made sense to me. I had been witnessing first-hand that the key presenting symptom in MedPsych illness is not the pain or the weakness or any physical findings. It is loss of function.

Meanwhile, while I was busy reviewing two years' worth of Dani's medical records in Providence to prepare for her admission, Dani was thrilled to be honored back home in a school-wide "pep rally" for her bravery in the face of this misunderstood illness. On admission to our unit Dani proudly showed us the framed picture of herself getting a standing ovation from the crowd that had gathered in her school gymnasium. She was sitting at center court in her wheelchair, a large bouquet of flowers in her arms, smiling, waving. Dani kept the framed photo close to her at all times. That picture proved to herself and the world that she really was as physically debilitated as she felt she was. Illness identity in a lovely wooden frame.

I think it's fair to say that everyone in the gym that day, including Dani and her parents, were well intentioned. And yet we can all imagine how hard it would be to backpedal from such a spectacle.

"So, it turns out it was all my anxiety making me believe I couldn't walk ..."

In our first family meeting Mom turned into Mama Bear over the discussion of our (already agreed to) treatment plan and Dad shook his head:

"Maybe this isn't the right place for Dani. We know a lot of doctors don't really understand Ehlers-Danlos. We're still learning about it ourselves. Maybe we need to look somewhere else for help."

None of the doctors sitting around the table brought up the evaluation at Boston Children's. By this time, that made perfect sense to me. Everybody at the table knew that's why she ended up with us. Debating diagnoses was not only useless but beside the point. We didn't need to prove Dani didn't have Ehlers-Danlos. We hoped that the family would allow us to help her improve her physical and emotional function. Diagnostic clarity would follow.

And what if all of us New Englanders really had missed the diagnosis? What if Dani turned out to develop some objective features of Ehlers-Danlos? That wouldn't have changed her therapeutic plan a bit. There was still no need for her to be in a wheelchair. She still didn't need to be out of school. She still needed her emotional brain and her cognitive brain to be having better conversations.

Dani's first few weeks on MedPsych, were marked, as they often were, by extreme treatment resistance. Our job was mostly psychoeducation about emotionally based illness and a lot of emotional support. My role specifically was to coordinate and integrate physical and occupational therapy into the psychiatric treatment and to reinforce the validating language of recovery—with total conviction.

"We know this is hard. We know your symptoms are real. Your physical exam is very reassuring. We can keep you safe while we get your legs working again. We need to keep going."

At first this evoked a stream of expletives—a common reaction on the unit even from otherwise soft-spoken young girls with pigtails and sweet graphics on their T-shirts. The family hung on by a thread. Week two, Dani's favorite nurse, Diane, reported in rounds that Dani wanted a different pediatrician on her case.

"Dr. Kozel is mean," Diane announced to the room with a grin.

Dani had continued to lose weight and I had spoken to her about the importance of nutrition as we worked to improve her stamina. This was not well received. Her poor stamina was due to Ehlers-Danlos, she explained to me, not her nutrition or the fact that she spent all day in a wheelchair. I was learning to take it all in stride. On the bright side we heard she had started to open up a little bit to her psychologist, and occupational therapy reported she was requiring much less assistance to use the bathroom than she did at home, apparently out of a desire for privacy. Her parents, by all accounts, had grown a little calmer but still needed daily reminders of why we were all sticking to the plan.

Week three, Dani shouted at me to get out of her room. At the same time, she had made a couple of friends on the unit and was beating them all at cards. Physical therapy announced that she was standing up and bearing weight for a few seconds, with assistance. Her psychologist, Dr. Pelletier, reported she was starting to talk more about her depression. We heard from staff that Dani reached out in kind support of a fellow patient during group therapy. Her parents, seeing Dani become more energized and independent, admitted to a glimmer of hope.

Week four, Dani asked me if I could give her something to help her menstrual cramps. Well of course I could, and did, and that helped pull me out of the doctor dumpster she had placed me in. This drifted naturally into broader issues of sexual health. She had lots of great questions, and I had lots of clear answers. A few days later she listened pretty closely when I explained what her physical exam was telling me. Her skin was nice and taut, not loose, and she showed no signs of the excessive bruising that can be seen with Ehlers-Danlos. She had no unusual facial features. Her joints appeared stable. I could see why the Ehlers-Danlos specialist in Boston found no signs of the illness in Dani, but I didn't say that. It was enough that Dani was keenly interested in what her body was telling us.

This was not a scheming family. The idea that they had convinced hundreds of generous parents, teachers, and students of their daughter's diagnosis of Ehlers-Danlos when it was actually an emotionally driven illusion was too horrifying for them to contemplate. The reality was that few people would give Dani points for courage in fighting an emotionally driven illness the way they so eagerly did when she was nestled in her wheelchair with some elusive medical diagnosis. That is one of the ironies of these disorders. The kids I've seen recover from MedPsych illness are some of the bravest kids I have ever known. They all deserve pep rallies.

Maria was another patient who came to us entrenched in illness identity. She was a thirteen-year-old with a smile the size of Texas—which was appropriate since that was her family's adopted home after emigrating from Nicaragua a few years earlier. Her father was a wealthy businessman who saw his family infrequently. Maria and her mother were very close and grew even closer—almost inseparable—after their move to the US. Her mother described Maria as respectful and obedient. There were no signs of rebellion in this young girl. Maria had been an excellent student in Nicaragua, but on arrival to the states had a series of intestinal illnesses of uncertain origin that caused her to lose weight and miss a lot of school. Her mother, a former beauty queen, was unhappy in this new land, and became quite anxious about Maria, keeping her home whenever she complained of abdominal pain. Both mother and daughter ate little and were losing weight. Maria's father wavered between alarm and impatience, and the parents were arguing more and more frequently.

Over the course of time Maria saw many specialists and had many tests and invasive procedures, biopsies, and dietary modifications. Nobody could find a cause for her abdominal pain and food refusal. Each negative result more firmly convinced mother and child that this was indeed a rare and dangerous illness. By the time they made it to their regional children's hospital for a consult with a surgeon, Maria had lost 10 percent of her body weight, and the surgeon diagnosed her with something called gastroparesis—essentially meaning the stomach muscles were too weak to process food. Unfortunately, he recommended she have a gastrostomy feeding tube placed, despite the fact that the tissue throughout her entire GI tract appeared normal. The family agreed, and an illness identity was born.

One of the most frustrating parts about this blindness to emotionally driven illness on the part of medical providers is that with each test, each attempt at treating the physical symptoms, even if it's just to prove to the parents that everything's okay, the physical manifestations of the illness are likely to get worse, not better. Maria's external world kept validating that the physical symptoms were due to physical malfunction, despite the absence of any medical evidence. Why else was it warranting such an intense level of investigation? Maria and her mom were hearing that they were right to keep pursuing medical diagnoses and treatments. And now that they had a diagnosis—gastroparesis—they clung to like it was the Holy Grail.

Gastroparesis is a condition that can be caused by a number of factors, especially if there is damage to a patient's vagal nerve. Diabetes is a well-known cause of this dysfunction. But the first diagnostic consideration in an otherwise healthy young patient with gastroparesis should be a restrictive eating disorder. Maria's providers in Texas missed the opportunity to address her (and it turned out, her mother's) eating disorder and did considerable harm by looking for a surgical solution.

One of my tasks as the pediatrician on the team would be to help the family understand just what gastroparesis was. It was a loss of functional tone in the stomach that can be due to lack of use. The treatment was to slowly reinstitute normal oral feedings, to gradually build up the stomach's muscle tone again. Putting in a feeding tube was the worst possible solution. It would be like telling someone who has weak leg muscles from sitting around all day to be careful not to move around too much. Their legs are too weak.

Maria's reaction to over-medicalization was typical—even diagnostic—for MedPsych illness. The more medical intervention the patient received—X-rays, endoscopies, medication trials; appointments, appointments, appointments—the less functional she became. So it is not the least bit surprising that when Maria had some modest weight gain on the formula that now ran through her feeding tube, she went on to develop new kinds of symptoms to replace the old ones that had kept her home from school. Generalized weakness and pain of an unknown source left her almost bedridden. Her circadian rhythms regressed to that of an infant's. She required her mother's constant, fretting attention. Maria and her mother were frightened and bewildered, circling the wagons, and her father was getting very frustrated, usually from afar.

Maria threw me off for a moment in our first family meeting. My immediate impression was that of a gentle fawn—thin, fragile looking, helpless. She offered a wan smile in response to our pleasantries—right up until the point where we started talking about the treatment plan. When I began explaining how we would gradually be reintroducing solid foods, tiny Maria responded in a rather imperious tone that I obviously didn't understand gastroparesis and should call her specialists in Texas so they could explain it to me. It turned out she was more like a little pink porcupine than a gentle fawn, and this, no surprise, was going to be a prickly ride. But the longer I worked in MedPsych the more I came to expect this resistive response—no different than expecting to see a nasty red pharynx in someone with strep throat.

Like many families that come to our unit, referred from major medical centers across the country, Maria and her family were expecting pizzazz when they got to us—tests that nobody else had thought of, diagnoses that nobody else could pronounce, a plan that would help Maria live her best life despite her physical debilitation. Instead they got me in my corduroys and clogs and a bunch of other ordinary-appearing providers speaking about things like somatic symptom disorders, and how our goal was to return Maria to normal nutritional function while supporting her and her family emotionally in the process. Maria's reaction, as well as that of her parents, closely paralleled Dani's. It was a recognizable pattern. These illnesses may be born of the deflection of emotional pain, but they gird themselves with illness identity and sustain themselves with treatment resistance.

So what follows for us is a careful dance to meet the family where they are. They were quite loving and appropriately concerned about Maria's current condition as well as her future. They were all frightened to some degree, and mistrustful of medical providers in general. Adding to that mix was a common subtext: If their child's devastating illness was emotionally based, what does that have to say about their parenting? What does it say about all the invasive tests, all the missed school, and—good god—the gastrostomy tube that was currently sticking out of her perfectly healthy abdominal wall?

We let them know that we hear what they are telling us, that we know they love her and know her much better than we do. We talked about what the illness has done to all of them. And we told them we are convinced we could help Maria. This meant restoring age-appropriate independence, healthier eating behaviors, and the ability to participate in school and other typical adolescent activities.

I knew now not to argue diagnoses. But I also knew she no more needed a feeding tube than an overweight kid who gets winded in gym class needs to avoid physical activity. I explained that at this point in Maria's course of illness and past evaluations, we were very confident that she had a healthy GI tract and believed that the ineffectual stomach contractions known as gastroparesis were not the reason she could not eat, but rather the exact opposite. Her stomach muscles were simply weak from disuse. The treatment was for Maria to eat. We would restore function by gradually reintroducing solid foods by mouth. We believed that by combining that with a psychologically therapeutic environment, under close medical monitoring, Maria would recover. It was that simple—and that difficult. I did not get into eating disorder treatment beyond what we would implement to restore her GI function. The MedPsych unit was not an eating disorder program. We unraveled the over-medicalization, and brought the underlying disorder to the forefront. But specialized eating disorder treatment would need to take place elsewhere once Maria was ready for discharge from our Inpatient program.

It was then time for me to take a step back, and for the behavioral team, the nutritionists, and physical, occupational, and speech therapists to chime in. We warned the parents that the first two weeks would likely be the hardest—that Maria's emotional brain will be screaming at her to not let this happen. But a slow pace, patience, hopefulness, and teamwork would keep us all moving forward. So would success.

Success took almost two months of intense emotional support, conflict, acting out, and always, always the dance of taking two steps forward, one step back. It is the way of MedPsych treatment. Maria had to restore her eating function, rebuild her stamina, and confront the scary emotions she had been so disconnected from. With emotional health also came healthier, more developmentally appropriate relationships within her family. All this had to happen for Maria to be able to let go of that tenacious illness identity that the diagnosis of gastroparesis had burdened her with. Her reward was that she did recover her own identity as a smart, friendly teen who liked boys, excelled in schoolwork, and wished her parents would stay out of her business. Her parents began to see how they were reacting to Maria's illness rather than to Maria, and they learned how to better support her and each other.

MedPsych work is slow, and full of conflict. Its methods can seem very perplexing to patients and their families, but the experience from the front line is that the patterns of illness are very predictable and the treatment methods that define it are highly effective. The principles of treatment also clarify what should have happened earlier on in Maria's evaluations. Maria had started out as a pretty healthy outpatient and could likely have remained an outpatient if she had access to Med-Psych-informed treatment right from the beginning from her PCP. And if she had been referred to a MedPsych-informed pediatric GI specialist they would have made it clear that psychological support was all part of the package. No one would have sent her to a surgeon. But her course took her down a road of over-medicalization and unhelpful diagnoses that would only make matters worse and her condition much harder to treat.

MedPsych-informed outpatient care, starting with the PCP, is a key component to effectively managing emotionally based illnesses.

CHAPTER 23

Factitious Illness and Other Fictions

T O UNDERSTAND MEDPSYCH ILLNESS WE HAVE TO acknowledge the intricate, mysterious connections between the human brain and its transport system—the rest of the body. We know neuroscientists have been making extraordinary inroads into mapping the brain genetically, chemically, and functionally. These discoveries, although slow to make it out to the rest of us mere mortals, are informing and redefining the way clinicians approach everything from illness to education, sexuality, and personality. It is wondrous and humbling. The distinction between "mind" and "body" now reminds me of the observation made by numerous astronauts when they have looked back at earth: there are no borders on earth, only those artificial divisions assigned by humans. Neuroscience is inviting clinicians and patients alike to step out of established orbits, get a glimpse of the wholeness of a person, and realize that while it might, at times, be necessary to distinguish between our back pain and our mood, the reality is that these distinctions are humanity's ways of organizing thoughts more than they are a human being's reality.

To organize our thoughts more clearly around MedPsych illness, it might be helpful to draw another border for ourselves—what Med-Psych is, and what it is not.

Consider Veronica. She is sixteen years old, sociable, likes school well enough but appreciates the social aspects of it far more than the intellectual stimulation. Her parents ground her once a month on average, often related to avoiding her school responsibilities in various and imaginative ways. Today she has a "total-waste-of-time" term paper due that she hasn't even started. She draws her fluffy bathrobe close around her, rumples her hair, sets her facial features into sad zombie mode, and stirs her hot tea with a thermometer. A few minutes later as her mother flies into the kitchen preparing to leave for work, Veronica appears to remove the hot thermometer from her mouth and hands it to her mom, murmuring hoarsely, "I'm so sick."

She is clearly faking it. Her mom may or may not know. But Veronica knows. You can practically hear the TV laugh track in the background.

This subterfuge deserves the label *factitious behavior.* First, it is intentional. The would-be patient is clearly aware that she is faking it and is consciously doing it for a clear purpose. There is no reason to suspect a psychiatric disorder here. She is not feigning this fever because she is desperate to avoid school or social relationships, or because her emotional needs have regressed to that of a much younger child, but rather to avoid consequences. This is not, in itself, a psychiatric illness. This is most likely a maturation issue. She might very well have some performance anxiety around schoolwork, and anxiety begets procrastination as sure as colds produce mucous. So yes, we're aware that there is an emotional component. At the same time we all remain quite hopeful for Veronica that this will not evolve into a chronic maladaptive coping skill and we are gratified to hear in the supermarket five years hence that she just loves her new job as a second-grade teacher.

Since there is not a psychiatric illness at the root of Veronica's behavior this is not a MedPsych disorder. The patient is intentionally faking the symptoms for an express purpose in a limited way that has minimal impact on her overall ability to function. If she has a track record of anxiety and procrastination she may benefit from a little therapy, or it may only require Mom to retake the temp and have a heart-to-heart talk with Veronica about what the heck is going on. This brings us to another clarifying term. If this sort of behavior evolves into a calculated pattern as an *adult* of faking an illness for personal gain, and Veronica develops a track record of manipulating the medical community into keeping her on endless disability, then this is what is known as *malingering*. Maladaptive yes, but still very much in the conscious, intentional realm. So again, not a MedPsych illness.

To recap, Veronica's behavior is conscious, intentional, with a clear goal in mind, and in an individual who otherwise is functioning in a pretty healthy way. Not a psychiatric illness.

What if things get more complicated? Suppose twelve-year-old Justin has had a really tough time starting middle school. He's always struggled in school due to some mild learning disabilities. He tends to be anxious, and has trouble making friends. A year earlier he had recurrent abdominal pains that kept him out of sixth grade on and off for several weeks. His nutrition remained stable and there were no significant clinical findings. It eased up over the summer. He had been otherwise healthy except for chronic nasal allergies. So far it sounds as if he might have a lot in common with Eleanor. But his story is more tangled.

Justin is being raised by his grandparents who are having trouble making ends meet and are worried about eviction from their apartment. He lives with them after being removed from his mother's care as a toddler due to her traumatizing neglect.

One Monday morning, shortly after he started seventh grade, Justin spit up bright red blood into the toilet. His grandparents were understandably alarmed and worried this was related to his history of abdominal pain. His pediatrician sent him to a pediatric GI specialist and the initial workup was reassuring. The consensus from the PCP and the GI specialist was that the episode was probably due to a nosebleed and swallowed blood. But Justin continued to spit up/vomit blood on a regular basis, and in increasing amounts. His frightened grandparents kept him home from school and continued to seek medical attention over the next several weeks. Providers started noticing how traumatized the areas around his nail beds and inside his nostrils were. As his symptoms escalated, unexplained cuts on his lips and the roof of his mouth were also noted. He adamantly denied any self-harm. Then one day his grandmother found a razor blade in the pocket of his jeans. The dam broke and the truth poured out of Justin in a torrent of tears. He had been doing this to be able to stay home and keep his grandparents close by to avoid the bullying horror show that was his school day and the full-blown panic of separation anxiety in a kiddo who had suffered traumatic events in early childhood.

This is *factitious disorder*. That word, disorder, is an important distinction from Veronica's brand of ditching school. On the one hand, Justin, like Veronica, knows he is not bleeding from a medical illness. There is conscious intent and purpose on the part of the patient. However, unlike Veronica, his efforts were driven by emotional desperation and involved significant self-harm. In addition, they not only persisted but escalated over time. As such, it produced significant shifts in the family dynamics, in which grandparents found themselves focusing more and more attention on the bleeding while typical expectations that a guardian has for a child that age—going to school, making friends, being increasingly self-reliant—were shelved for the time being. Justin, who had already suffered significant psychical trauma and neglect, was using these very maladaptive coping skills in order to avoid the agony of his school experience, and to find comfort in the emotional support the illness elicited from his fretting grandparents.

Factitious disorder, in contrast to Veronica's less dangerous efforts, is a psychiatric illness that presents with worrisome, potentially harmful, self-induced medical symptoms due to overpowering distress and emotional need. The patient is aware of what he is doing, but this behavior is extreme and dangerous—causing himself repeated injury and ramping up an army of medical specialists which in turn resulted in needless, aggressive medical procedures. All of this suggests Justin is suffering from overwhelming emotional distress and a distorted idea of self-preservation.

Justin was admitted to the MedPsych unit because we could keep him safe in a highly therapeutic environment, but also with the pediatric support needed to coordinate his care with all the medical specialties that had been previously called upon to assess the unexplained bleeding. It also required an intense integration of behavioral intervention for the child and the family, strong school support, and compassionate medical monitoring.

As we move along the emotional spectrum of symptoms that cannot be explained on a medical basis we come to *somatization.* It is a phenomenon well known to parents, teachers, school nurses, and pediatricians that begins to move us into the more typical presentations of emotionally based illness. *Somatization* refers to physical complaints that arise from feeling your emotions through your body. Often it presents in a mild form. Eleanor, the eight-year-old with recurrent Sunday evening tummy aches, presents a good example of somatization. She otherwise seems to be healthy and functioning pretty well in all the ways we expect to see eight-year-olds navigate their days. Mom and Dad are supportive, and once they accept that there is an emotional basis for these symptoms, get her to talk about school and any worries she may have about that. They keep her teacher updated as well. Her parents provide soothing skills like reading or singing to help her get to sleep on school nights. When the sun rises on Monday morning, Eleanor may still be worried about school, but she is armed with both daylight and some coping tools that will help her to master her anxieties in small steps.

What puts this in the emotional illness category? Eleanor's presentation is different than Veronica's in that she is *not* faking it. She is actually experiencing the kind of anxiety that is common in childhood, but so hard for a child to articulate. She is, in a relatively mild but very *real* way, experiencing her emotions through her body. Secondly, she has no conscious end goal. She's not trying to avoid long division. She may or may not even realize she's worried about school. Either way she is not able to connect the two things—her anxiety about school and the troublesome belly pain. Grownups will need to help her draw a line between her fears and her symptoms.

Somatization is an example of mild emotionally driven illness that can often be readily treated. When the process requires a greater degree of professional support, such as a therapist or even a partial day program, we're more likely to use the term somatic symptom *disorder.*

Annie provides a good example of this. She is a nine-year-old with recurrent generalized headaches. Her mother acknowledges that she herself is an anxious person, and she tends to worry a lot about Annie's ailments which have included a "sensitive stomach" that produces nausea and vomiting when she's nervous. Her father is a high-functioning alcoholic. Annie was followed closely by her PCP for her headaches and was seen by a pediatric neurologist. Physical exam, laboratory tests, and a CT scan were all normal and reassuring. With each new round of normal studies Annie's symptoms seem to intensify, especially as Annie started missing more school. Her mother grew frustrated that "nobody can figure this out." She took family medical leave from work and was thinking of quitting so that she could homeschool Annie. Mom and Dad argued about this. Annie reported that she missed going to school and worried about all the work she was missing.

To recap Annie's situation, there is a history of physical reactions to anxiety, there is parental anxiety and conflict, disruption of age appropriate social function (school), and disruption of family function (work and income). The more reassuring the workup was, the more the symptoms intensified. Unaddressed alcoholism is of course another red flag. We now see this constellation of presentations as typical of emotionally based illness. Her symptoms are more entrenched than in Emily's case, and will require more intense behavioral intervention. They would be characterized as somatic symptom disorder. Annie was ultimately referred to Hasbro's Partial MedPsych program and was successfully transitioned back to school after four weeks of individual and family therapies, with the family agreeing to continue therapy as outpatients.

These days many pediatric subspecialists are well-versed in the psychological components of symptoms in childhood illness. Pediatric gastroenterologists in fact refer to the gut as "the second brain" in acknowledgment of the close relationships between our emotions and our GI health. This applies as much to children with identifiable GI pathology, such as ulcerative colitis, as it does to children like Annie and Eleanor with no medical explanations for their debilitating symptoms. Integrating behavioral health into medical health does not mean under-medicalizing children who need medical intervention. It is a parallel process that explores "What impact are your medical issues having on your mood and relationships and quality of life?" And just as importantly, "To what extent is your mood and anxiety impacting your physical symptoms?" We don't have to have all the answers before we start integrating care. In fact, that is the worst thing we could wait for. There is a limitless supply of medical tests and procedures that could be offered to families desperate for a "medical" explanation. Waiting to exhaust all possible medical avenues before addressing the emotional factors can be disastrous, as it was for little Maria from Texas. Each new negative test or wishy-washy result only increases the anxiety and therefore the symptoms.

This is why pediatricians, neurologists, gastroenterologists, cardiologists, and a growing number of other specialties recognize when to take a pause. As a result, it has become more common to have psychological services embedded into these outpatient subspecialty clinics. We know to explain to parents and patient that the child's inability to do what other children of her age can do because of illness deserves behavioral and therapeutic support, regardless of the cause—whether it's anxiety, inflammatory bowel disease, or a congenital heart malformation. We also point out that emotionally driven illness affects the whole family—including siblings—and should be treated as such. And we hope to earn the family's trust that we will be ever vigilant for new symptoms or indications of disease and will pursue that alongside behavioral interventions.

Having said that, it's a messy business. Teenagers are not above faking a fever to ditch school. Traumatized kids will injure themselves to get the attention they crave. And third graders will be duped by their emotional brains into experiencing abdominal pain. Humans are messy. Families are especially messy. And worried families can be the messiest of all. Earning a family's trust in these situations is a constant struggle to move faster and in a straighter direction than the symptoms do.

CHAPTER 24

One Giant Leap

M Y SIXTH-FLOOR OFFICE ON THE MEDPSYCH UNIT HAD A
big picture window looking over Narragansett Bay to the east.
I rarely sat still long enough to enjoy it during daylight, but as
night fell I'd make my way back to my desk, and I'd stare out at the soothing darkness after a mind-boggling day. My favorite sight of all was a rising
moon looking down over us, reminding us that we are part of something
much bigger than a desk, a potted plant, a framed picture.

The moon is apart from us and yet ever-present, whether we can
actually see it or not. Even in this age of astonishing rocketry it seems so
out of reach to the average human. Out of reach, and yet its most obvious influence on us, moonlight, has been an inspiration to us throughout human history. We know it is real, and yet what we see is only a
reflection of the sun's light.

The moon does more than shine light on us. We know that it constantly pulls on us, just as we pull on the moon to hold it close. We
know it influences us because we can see the results. The inhales and
exhales of the oceans are observable. The sea changes can be explained

and predicted. We don't have any control over rising and falling seas, and most of the time we are not conscious of the moon's role. And even though we package its influence as gravitational force, we don't really know what that is in any fundamental way either. All we know is what we observe, like how masses behave. And how seas behave as a result.

This, for me, parallels the nature of MedPsych illness. Neuroscience has been exploding in recent decades, and the pathways by which our brains produce thoughts and feelings—what we call the mind—are slowly but surely emerging. Yet at the clinical level of doctor and patient we mostly surmise what is going on in the brain by the way its remarkable pedestal, the rest of the body, behaves.

MedPsych work taught me that the experience of emotionally driven symptoms is as real as the invisible pain of a broken arm. As real as the invisible force of gravity. The actual interface between anxiety and the unexplained inability of a patient to walk or talk or eat food may still elude us, but we understand clinically what types of circumstances allow these illnesses to take hold and just as importantly, what makes them better—just as folks knew, long before Sir Isaac Newton shared his thoughts, that the sea is changeable, that there are times to go fishing, and times to stay on the beach.

I will be forever grateful for the opportunity to do MedPsych work. I came to it as a late career pediatrician who thought she had seen just about everything. My colleagues at Hasbro handed me a telescope and stood at my side as I discovered for myself the powers that the oldest, most primitive parts of our brain hold. And I saw as well how my previous practice had been filled with milder versions of these illnesses—back when I still believed that the body didn't lie, that the emotional brain was limited in its reach. But now I know better, just as I know that the mysterious force of gravity prevents us from floating around our backyards even though I can't explain why.

Neuroscience will continue to tease out the pathways by which Eleanor's separation anxiety turned to physical pain on Monday mornings, as well as the more problematic pathways that caused Mike to fall in a convulsive heap at school every day. Maybe my baby granddaughter will be doing her tenth-grade science project on the mapping of those pathways someday. But for the moment all we have is the knowledge that these forces are there, and recognizing that, we can predict how to get our patients back to a healthier life.

The important point here is that we know enough now to effectively treat children that have emotionally based disorders. Yet even the current understanding of the nature of these illnesses is slow to move out of the academic medical centers and into the awareness of frontline medical providers, parents, and teachers. But the knowledge does exist, and the principles underlying the diagnosis and treatment of MedPsych illness need to be part of pediatric residency training. It only makes sense. These disorders make up a large part of not only general pediatric practice, but of pediatric neurology, pediatric GI, pediatric orthopedics, pediatric cardiology, and many other specialties.

At Hasbro Children's Hospital, pediatric residents would spend one morning of their Adolescent Medicine rotation shadowing me. That was one morning out of a three-year training program. My own training had similar imbalances. I could intubate a twenty-six-week preemie with confidence (something I was never called on to do in my subsequent practice), but my total child psychiatry training was made up of monthly noontime lectures—lectures I would sleep through if I had been on call the night before.

One thing that all pediatricians can agree on is that now, more than ever before, many of our children are in psychological peril. A great deal of pediatric research suggests that the false universe of social media has pulled the rug out from under many vulnerable children and adolescents over the past decade, resulting in an alarming rise in the rate of pediatric depression and suicide. Anxiety disorders in the pediatric population are now at an all-time high. The scourge of mass school shootings is only pouring more gasoline onto that fire.

Those of us who work with children and adolescents—parents and doctors, teachers and nurses—cannot make our society less toxic to children. So we need to arm ourselves with the best knowledge that current neuropsychology and psychiatric medicine offer for prevention and treatment. That means, among other things, incorporating Med-Psych practice into pediatric training. It means providing psychoeducation to families starting at a young age. It means doing away with medical excuses for school absences, and putting social-emotional competency for students on an educational front burner.

It means a moonshot.

The End

About the Author

Dr. Maggie Kozel, a graduate of Georgetown University Medical School, is a pediatrician and author. She has spent most of her professional life in primary care pediatrics and has taken great pride in translating a pediatrician's perspectives into the written word. Her first book, *The Color of Atmosphere*, won an Independent Publishers' silver medal for writing in healthcare. She has been an activist for healthcare equity and common sense gun safety, and her numerous commentaries have appeared in outlets such as the *New York Times* and *Huffington Post*.

In 2015 Dr. Kozel accepted a position as the Medical Director of the Inpatient MedPsych unit at Hasbro Children's Hospital in Providence, Rhode Island. In doing this MedPSych work Dr. Kozel realized she had been treating emotionally-based symptoms in her previous outpatient practice with one hand tied behind her back. In this time of pediatric mental health crisis Dr. Kozel's passion for writing from a pediatrician's viewpoint shifted to what patients' stories teach us about the emotional brain and the basic skill set that all pediatricians, educators, and parents need to effectively manage pediatric anxiety and school-avoidant behaviors.

Dr. Kozel lives with her husband, Randy, also a physician, in Jamestown RI, has two daughters, and spends as much time as possible on her bike. You can find her anytime at www.MaggieKozelMD.com.

Made in the USA
Middletown, DE
12 July 2023